Julia Whitney
656-0409

FAMILY THERAPY AND EVALUATION THROUGH ART

FAMILY THERAPY AND EVALUATION THROUGH ART

By

HANNA YAXA KWIATKOWSKA, A.T.R.

Assistant Professor
The George Washington University
Graduate School of Arts and Sciences

Formerly

Head Art Therapy Unit, Consultant
Adult Psychiatry Branch
National Institute of Mental Health

With a Foreword by

LYMAN C. WYNNE, M.D., Ph.D.

Professor of Psychiatry and
Director of the Division of Family Programs
Chairman of the Department of Psychiatry
University of Rochester School of
Medicine and Dentistry
Rochester, New York

and

ADELE R. WYNNE, A.B.

Art Therapist
Rochester Psychiatric Center
Rochester, New York

CHARLES C THOMAS • PUBLISHER
Springfield • *Illinois* • *U.S.A.*

Published and Distributed Throughout the World by
CHARLES C THOMAS • PUBLISHER
BANNERSTONE HOUSE
301-327 East Lawrence Avenue, Springfield, Illinois, U.S.A.

© *1978, by* CHARLES C THOMAS • PUBLISHER
ISBN 0-398-03729-9
Library of Congress Catalog Card Number: 77-12001

With THOMAS BOOKS *careful attention is given to all details of
manufacturing and design. It is the Publisher's desire to present
books that are satisfactory as to their physical qualities and artistic
possibilities and appropriate for their particular use.* THOMAS
BOOKS *will be true to those laws of quality that assure a good
name and good will.*

Any part of this book may be re-
printed royalty free for U.S.
Government purposes.

Printed in the United States of America
N-1

Library of Congress Cataloging in Publication Data

Kwiatkowska, Hanna Yaxa.
    Family therapy and evaluation through art.

    Bibliography: p.
    Includes index.
    1. Art therapy.   2. Family psychotherapy.
I. Title.
RC489.A7K93   616.8'916   77-12001
ISBN 0-398-3729-9

To My Husband

1958

FOREWORD

THE FIELD of psychotherapy has been a proliferation of new theories and techniques in the last quarter of a century. Some flowered brilliantly, only to wither or at least never become firmly established in the bedrock of accepted therapeutic approaches. Art therapy has withstood the test of time and has grown to be recognized as a major therapeutic and diagnostic tool in working with a wide spectrum of pathologies. Hanna Yaxa Kwiatkowska has wedded the established concepts and practice of art therapy for the individual with the more recent theories and techniques of family therapy. Her carefully elaborated synthesis of these two disciplines is a significant new hybrid which brings into view underlying aspects of family structure and dynamics, provides a modality for lively participation by all family members together in therapy, and builds a graphic and much needed record of family change over time. This book will be basic for those in the field who are interested in keeping abreast of the expanding role of art therapy as either a primary or an adjunctive approach in working with families.

It has been our privilege and deep pleasure to know Hanna Kwiatkowska on both professional and personal levels during the twenty years in which the work on family and art therapy described in this volume evolved. Previously, she had established her personal artistic credentials as a prize-winning sculptress in Europe and Brazil and had entered the field of art therapy in its founding days with Margaret Naumburg. Hanna Kwiatkowska then joined the intramural staff of the National Institute of Mental Health in a golden period of its history. For a decade, beginning in the middle to late 1950s, unprecedented recruiting, budgeting, and administrative flexibility enabled the Intramural Research Program of NIMH to become an unique environment for creative exploration in fields widely ranging from biochemistry of the brain to studies of social class in relation to mental illness. In this setting, as Head of the Art Therapy Unit in the Adult Psychiatry Branch, Hanna Kwiatkowska could join with colleagues across traditional disciplinary boundaries in studies of schizophrenia, families and family therapy, and adolescent development. The flow of ideas to and from her Art Therapy Unit gave insights and impetus to the staff of these varied programs and at the same time provided her with the freedom to apply her innovative and integrative talents with a diversity of families whom she knew over time and with a distinctive depth of understanding.

In more recent years, Hanna Kwiatkowska has served as a teacher and consultant based in the George Washington University and the Washington School of Psychiatry, simultaneously contributing to workshops, exhibits, and demonstrations at numerous universities, psychiatric centers, and professional meetings throughout America and elsewhere in the world. Perhaps most notably, she was received with great enthusiasm in Brazil as a three-time holder of a Fulbright Travel Award.

The vivid and enduring personal experience with individuals and families provided by evaluation and therapy through art appropriately constitutes the core of this book. The case histories illuminate the text with examples of the individual and family art productions associated with a wide range of patients and their families. Particular emphasis is given to the problems of integrating family art therapy with the various verbal therapies which the individual or family may be concurrently receiving. Kwiatkowska's wide experience and theoretical background have led her to postulate and courageously employ new techniques to overcome the resistance to exploring art as a medium for communication and self-expression, resistance not only by the patient and his family but often by staff members trained in other disciplines. With the patient or family seen in verbal therapy by another therapist, she made the startling but brilliant suggestion that the verbally oriented therapist, untrained in art techniques, be integrated into the art therapy as cotherapist. This serves to awaken the verbally oriented therapist to the evaluative and therapeutic significance of the family's artistic productions and unifies the total treatment approach. Even more daring and innovative are her instructions to encourage the cotherapist to join in artistic expression of his feelings along with the family. This "joining" with the family has many practical consequences.

Especially useful are her detailed instructions for the Evaluative Family Art Session. Six different pictures are requested of the family; the theoretical rationale for the change of instructions for each picture is explained in the text. Interpretation of the resulting pictures from the viewpoints of symbolism and family dynamics draws upon her wide background in concepts of individual art therapy and conventional verbal family therapy.

For the research-oriented reader, her concluding chapters summarize a variety of ways art therapy may be analyzed to give statistical or empirical validity to diagnostic hypotheses. Her involvement in three varied research studies suggests approaches that others may want to pursue. She acknowledges that the results are preliminary and in some cases still inconclusive. Artistic renditions, like verbal productions, are difficult to categorize. Systematic research in the art therapy field has been rare; Hanna Kwiatkowska's contributions are pioneering efforts.

Time and time again, one obtains the sense of gratification and therapeutic effectiveness which arise from involvement in art therapy which provides an opportunity to record permanently an emotional experience. Reviewing the pictures later allows the therapist and the family to gain perspective and distance on a feeling that may have been too difficult to acknowledge at the time of creation. By returning to a picture, continuity and focus on a problem can be maintained through as many sessions as needed until individual distortions are clarified or catharsis is achieved. Like the artistic renderings of the family in therapy, this book will remain etched in the mind of all who take the time to read it. A gifted art therapist has used the tools of her trade, her wise, critical intelligence, and her warm and compassionate personal qualities to convey to us innovative and significant contributions in the blossoming field of family art therapy.

LYMAN C. WYNNE, M.D., Ph.D.
ADELE R. WYNNE, A.B.

INTRODUCTION

IN MY FOURTEEN YEARS as art therapist at the National Institute
of Mental Health in Bethesda, Maryland, beginning in 1958,
using art media for therapy and evaluation of families, and in my
further work with families in other settings, I accumulated an
enormous volume of material. I feel the time has come to share
with others what I experienced and learned through this work.

While reviewing the families' pictures and sculptures, I was
impressed with the freshness and liveliness with which I reexperi-
enced the sessions at which the artwork was produced. But when
I then turned to my written notes and to the tape recordings of
the sessions, I soon realized that my being again so vividly in
touch with the emotions evoked during the sessions and with the
intensity of my relationship with the families resulted primarily
from their art productions. The verbal material served to clarify
and make more precise the meaning and message of the artwork,
but the memories awakened assumed a different character. The
strongly felt emotional impact gave way to scientific scrutiny, to
an intellectual desire to learn more and to understand better.
These two aspects of my experience while preparing the material
for this book may shed light on the mysterious and peculiar role
of art in the realm of human experience.

The purpose of this book is to describe how the special kind of
communication provided by the graphic or plastic media is being
used with families for therapy, evaluation and research. The two
disciplines, family therapy and art therapy, which merge in the
discipline described in this book, have in recent years been the
object of increasing interest, research and formal education. It
is with some hesitation that I draw a parallel between the development of these two disciplines. Family therapy is a complex out-
growth of child and adult psychotherapy and communication
theory, with such pioneers and masters as Nathan W. Ackerman,

xi

Donald Bloch, I. Boszormenyi-Nagy, John E. Bell, Murray Bowen, James V. Framo, Jay Haley, Don D. Jackson, R. McGregor, Salvador Minuchin, Norman L. Paul, Irving M. Ryckoff, Virginia M. Satir, R. Tharp, Carl A. Whitaker, Lyman C. Wynne, and Gerald H. Zuk, among others. Family therapy has a variety of theoretical orientations and a vast literature and numerous training centers, and reaches further and further into all mental health facilities and institutions.

Art therapy is older than family therapy but has developed more slowly. It is only since 1969 that formal education has existed in this field.

Although the practice of analytically oriented art therapy began in the late forties, the first years of its existence saw an uphill battle on the part of talented and determined individuals who realized the important contribution their approach could make to the field of mental health. Foremost among these pioneers was Margaret Naumburg. It was she who opened the eyes of the psychiatric world to the power of the image, not only as a reflection of the unconscious but also as a powerful therapeutic and diagnostic tool. Her first book, *Studies of the "Free" Art Expression of Behavior Problem Children and Adolescents as a Means of Diagnosis and Therapy*,[1] was published in 1947 and was followed in 1950 by another important book, *Schizophrenic Art: Its Meaning in Psychotherapy*.[2] Numerous studies dealing with psychotic art and with the psychological exploration of the creative process date from as far back as the end of the last century, but these two books mark the beginning of an important era; they establish an identity for art therapy as a direct mode of treatment and diagnosis.

I do not plan to present here a survey of the historical development of art therapy, but any writing in this field must recognize the work of those who struggled to establish a place for this new discipline.

I was privileged to take my first steps in art therapy under the guidance of Margaret Naumburg and am deeply conscious of her impact on the development of my thinking and the evolution of my initial theoretical formulations and technique. However, I was aware of how much I needed a solid background in psychology, psychiatry and psychoanalysis. Formal university training programs in art therapy did not exist at that time. The William Alanson White Institute in New York, where I was admitted as a student, gave me the invaluable opportunity to study under such teachers as Clara Thompson and Erich Fromm.

When I look back at my own search for a road in a field that was still very nebulous around 1950, I realize how fortunate I was to encounter people who not only enriched my understanding of the intricacies of the human mind but who also accepted me and trusted my ideas and experiments.

I remember my surprise and pleasure when I saw my name linked with that of the late Doctor Winfred Overholser, Superintendent of St. Elizabeths Hospital, in the authorship of an exhibit at the Second World Congress of Psychiatry in Zurich in 1957. I recall with gratitude my years at St. Elizabeths, where, from 1955 to 1958, with no official title, I was given the freedom to design my own programs. My work there aroused my interest in finding a way to make use of all the riches of the clinical material that I was collecting. The staff's response was very positive and encouraging. Doctor Leon Konchegul was my first cotherapist in using art with groups of patients there. It was during that period that I made my first attempt at designing a research project: a blind study of the influence of chlorpromazine (Thorazine®) on graphic expression of schizophrenic patients. I deeply appreciated the hospital staff's cooperation in the conduct of this pilot study.

Also during that period came my unforgettable meeting with Frieda Fromm-Reichman, which led to my association with the National Institute of Mental Health in 1958. There I encountered stimulation and understanding of how I could contribute to research on the role of the family in the etiology of mental illness, with special emphasis on schizophrenia.

Doctors Lyman C. Wynne and Juliana Day Franz, through their bold but profoundly scientific theoretical formulations, were an inspiration to my work. They gave me support through their trust in the validity of my methods and, above all, through their invaluable collaboration.

Recalling this initial phase, I want to express my appreciation also to Doctor Jay T. Shurley, Acting Chief of the Adult Psychiatry Branch at the time of my first contact with the National Institute of Mental Health; Doctor David Hamburg, Chief of the Adult Psychiatry Branch, who hired me as the first art therapist at the Institute; Doctor Seymour Perlin,[3] my first coauthor; Doctor Christian C. Beels,[4] who was the first to include my approach in his definitions and description of the different trends in family therapy, thus officially bringing family art therapy into the psychiatric literature. Doctors F. Gentry Harris and Loren R. Mosher[5] were the first two persons to recognize in the use of art with the family the possibility of results not obtainable otherwise; with both I conducted extensive therapeutic and diagnostic work with families of schizophrenics.

Doctor James K. Dent has special importance in another phase of the use of art media with families. He has devoted an enormous amount of work to a systematic computerized comparative analysis of material obtained from patients and families of different diagnostic classifications.

I wish to record my recognition of the many generations of young psychiatrists, clinical associates at the National Institute of Mental Health, with whom I collaborated through the years. Among them, I especially wish to express my appreciation to Doctor Irwin Taube for his participation in our joint work, described in Chapter V. Doctor William E. Bunney's interest in the completion of this book during my final years at the National Institute of Mental Health was of great encouragement to me.

Doctor Bernard I. Levy, Director of the Graduate Training Program in Art Therapy at The George Washington University, has recognized the significant value of Family Art Therapy and was the first to introduce it in a university curriculum. For this and for his most helpful advice throughout my writing of this book I am deeply grateful.

Elinor Ulman, who painstakingly went over the first draft of this book, provided me the benefit of her expertise as much as an art therapist as an editor. Marcie Giberman was instrumental, through her meticulous editorial work, in bringing the book into its final form. My sincere thanks to both.

I do not think I would have brought this book to completion without my husband's sustained encouragement and support. His insightful comments on its content enriched my own understanding of the experiences I was attempting to describe.

But my greatest gratitude is to the troubled families who accepted my efforts to understand and to help. They gave me their trust and afforded me increasing experience in reaching families in distress.

H.Y.K.

CONTENTS

xvii

Contents

FAMILY THERAPY AND
EVALUATION THROUGH ART

CHAPTER I

ORIGIN AND DEVELOPMENT
OF ART THERAPY WITH
FAMILIES OF MENTAL PATIENTS

THE INCLUSION of the family in art therapy had a natural birth and an evolutionary process of development. It was not designed as an experiment that might produce interesting, unusual data. I would instead define it as an experiential discovery in which data emerged spontaneously. The richness, freshness and variety of pictorial and behavioral material obtained from accidental participation of family members in patients' individual art sessions led me to recognize how much we could gain from a mode of communication with the family that was not exclusively verbal.

In the initial period of my work in the Adult Psychiatry Branch of the National Institute of Mental Health, I saw patients individually in art therapy as an adjunct to their individual psychotherapy. The first article on art therapy published by the Government Printing Office dates from this period and was based on this work.[3]

It was also at that time that research at the Adult Psychiatry Branch of the National Institute of Mental Health began to focus more and more on family relations and on the role of the family in the etiology of mental illness in general and of schizophrenia in particular. Participation of the family in conjoint family therapy became a prerequisite for admission of patients. This resulted in the frequent presence of family members, who came to the ward either for conjoint family psychotherapy or to visit their hospital-ized offspring or relative, and eventually led to informal contact between different family subsystems and the art therapist.

In several instances family members asked to see the patient's artwork. I quickly found, however, that my yielding to such re-quests was destructive to the patient. In my individual work with patients I encouraged spontaneous creation of pictures or sculp-tures and respected and accepted their work regardless of its form and content. Artwork varied from very crude images, naive but expressive attempts to convey a message, to painfully disturbing expressions of psychotic confusion and chaos.

The parents would be either critical of the former or shocked and repulsed by the latter. Questions such as "Why don't you draw a nice basket of fruit?" or ". . . a vase with flowers?" were frequently heard. Most painful were those instances in which the family members would dismiss a picture that was disturbing and confused, though for the patient dramatically loaded with sym-bolic meaning, with the exclamation, "How cute!"

After several such experiences I started to look for a solution that would not discourage the family from being interested in the patient's work but that would entail less risk of such total lack of understanding of the patient's experience. I decided to allow them to visit the art therapy room provided they agreed to par-ticipate in the artwork.

Following is a description of my first experience in the par-ticipation of a family member in an art therapy session.

Peggy Williams, twenty-four years old, with blond curly hair, blue eyes and a clear, fresh complexion, was hospitalized after about two years of increasing symptoms of psychiatric illness rang-ing from distractibility during conversation, preoccupation with fixed ideas and suspiciousness, to auditory hallucinations and withdrawal, interrupted by either silliness and giggling or angry, paranoid outbursts. She was seen in 124 individual art therapy sessions over a period of twenty-three months. About two and one-half months after the beginning of our sessions, her brother Philip participated in one of our meetings at Peggy's invitation.

I was intrigued by how much I learned about their relation-

Plate I.

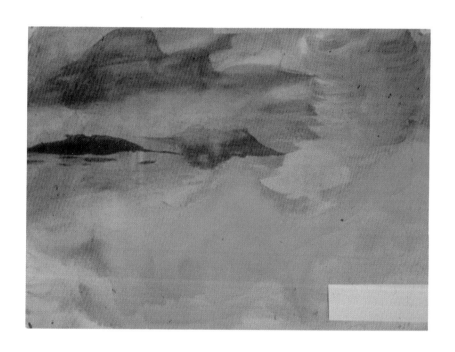

Plate II.

ship during this hour. When Peggy showed Philip her earlier pictures, he was moderately complimentary; then tension started to mount. To break it I suggested that they do a picture together. Philip accepted the suggestion enthusiastically and started to paint, showing Peggy the watercolor technique with which he was familiar (Plate I). Although Peggy's contribution to his painting was rather destructive, he tried to be gentle and patient with her. We can distinguish on their painting her short upward strokes at the bottom left and on the tree also at the left, and the patches she superimposed on the clouds, while where she did not interfere, the style is more static. I was impressed by the somber desolation of Philip's creation, which seemed to frighten his sister, who tried to add some brightness to it. Philip started the picture with the full, lighter tree on the left and ended with the desolate, dead tree on the right; we can see his mounting depression as he tried to adjust to his sister's behavior and to the destruction of his painting.

Philip called the picture "Wilderness," but Peggy insisted on "Desertion" or "Destitution," feelings constantly voiced when she spoke about being left in the hospital by her parents.

Their second joint picture was started by Peggy and was mostly painted by her (Plate II). Again we see the style of her brush strokes at the upper and lower right of the picture. She used gay, bright colors—red, orange and green—as if she were trying to escape from the dark desolation of the first picture. But Philip returned with his somber hue and tried to give the picture a realism more acceptable to him; the dark shapes on the upper left represent islands and mountains. He titled the picture "Mountains," while Peggy insisted on "Bali Hai," a kind of Shangri-la. Philip's depression was directly and forcefully expressed pictorially, while he escaped from its recognition through a literal title that did not evoke any emotional connotation.

Peggy's experience was of a different sort; she initially expressed her accusations of being abandoned by her family and left destitute, but then denied any despair or sadness in her life and sought escape into a formless fantasy of Shangri-la.

These two pictures were accurately expressive of this family's dynamics. The parents, especially the mother, persistently denied Peggy's illness. She hid from neighbors her daughter's hospitalization and her own harbored escape fantasies.

The father, like Philip, was better able to think coherently and to a degree to recognize reality. However, he was so enmeshed in paralyzing concreteness that he excluded any essential feeling that might have led to the exploration of and work on the problems he recognized and accepted only intellectually.

In a way Peggy mirrored her mother's psychology, and Philip, his father's.

The style and patterns of thinking in this family were unknown to me at the time of the brother-sister session, which immediately illustrated them so clearly.

A number of similar experiences in incidental participation of factions of families in art therapy sessions offered such a source of learning about families' relations and dynamics that family art therapy became an integral part of the Adult Psychiatry Branch program.

CHAPTER II

FAMILY ART TECHNIQUES AS THEY EVOLVED AT THE NATIONAL INSTITUTE OF MENTAL HEALTH*

A FTER THE early experiments discussed in the previous chapter, I was gradually able to design more definite techniques based on what we had observed and learned.

The programs in the Adult Psychiatry Branch of the National Institute of Mental Health into which family art techniques were gradually introduced were as follows: Family Studies; Adolescence and the Family; Twin and Siblings Study; School Project; Short-Term Family Therapy; and Special Project on Schizophrenia.

These programs were engaged in research investigating a population of broad diagnostic variety: schizophrenics (both chronic-process and reactive-acute) and their families; emotionally disturbed adolescents; monozygotic twins (concordant or discordant for schizophrenia) ; underachievers (School Project) ; and normal control families.

The studies were short and long term, ranging from three months to several years. The population investigated was in large part from the upper middle-class socioeconomic group, with edu-

---

*The format of the family art therapy described in this book is based largely on my experiences at the National Institute of Mental Health. The gradual exploration through the years of the intracacies of this program led me to generalize my findings as applicable to a variety of institutional settings.

cation ranging from grade school to doctoral degrees.

Basically three different uses of art media with families emerged. Each had its rationale, but all were designed so as to understand as much as possible the dynamics of families in different diagnostic categories for research and treatment.

We gradually developed three basic family art techniques:

1. Family art therapy as an adjunct to conjoint verbal family therapy.
2. Family art therapy as the primary mode of treatment (both types of family art therapy could be short or long term).
3. Family art evaluation.

As part of treatment the families' spontaneous art productions were intended to help family members and therapists to better understand the problems in the family, to clarify family members' roles and perceptions of each other, and to constitute a therapeutically useful mode of expression and communication.

Family art therapy became an integral part of the therapeutic program of the Family Studies Section and, during some periods, of the Section on Adolescence and the Family. The family art evaluation, which consisted of a single, more structured session, was gradually introduced into all the research projects mentioned earlier.*

In families admitted to these programs one member of each family presented psychopathological symptoms severe enough to require hospitalization in the psychiatric ward of the Clinical Center of the National Institutes of Health. Patients were admitted only on the condition that all members of the nuclear family agreed to participate as outpatients in all treatment and research procedures.

The nuclear family consisted of parents and siblings residing in the parental home. Married siblings participated either sporadically or, if they were still keeping strong ties with the family, on a regular schedule. Sometimes they were emotionally involved in the family problems to the detriment of their own marital relations.

---

*This technique is described in detail in Chapter VII.

The program for these families consisted of weekly conjoint family therapy sessions conducted by two psychiatrists or by a psychiatrist and a social worker acting as cotherapists. The patient was usually seen individually by one of the psychiatrists, and in some cases the parents were seen together in couple therapy by a social worker. The family also had to agree to undergo various psychological tests and other experimental procedures. The hospitalized family member participated in numerous ward activities, such as occupational and work therapy and ward meetings. The ward gradually became more and more community oriented, with the nursing staff taking leadership and playing a very active part.

When art therapy was introduced in 1958, it was conducted with patients individually. The frequency of sessions depended on each patient's needs and his responses to this form of therapy. The regressed, mute schizophrenic would at times be seen four or five times a week for short periods. Most of the patients were seen for an hour once or twice a week. In addition, formal group art therapy was intermittently conducted with small groups of patients by two art therapists on a weekly basis.[6]

As mentioned earlier, family art therapy gradually became one of the treatment procedures. From our initial tentative experiences with families in different configurations, we learned that it is best to see the whole nuclear family together from the beginning. Only in special cases did we see additional family members in the family art session or in subgroups. For example, we would invite to a session a member of the extended family who seemed to play an important role in family problems. Also, siblings who were married and had established their own homes or who lived in another part of the country and were visiting might be included. At times it was necessary to give support in individual sessions to a family member who had been attacked by other members, who was feeling particularly intimidated in the family group, or whose resistance was of such intensity that it paralyzed the rest of the family.

The adjunctive family art therapy session usually immediately preceded or followed the conjoint verbal family therapy. This format was as much for practical reasons as for therapeutic strategy. Many of the families came from distant suburban areas, one or both parents were working, and siblings were going to school. Even one trip a week required a considerable amount of their time and effort.

But besides this practical aspect, there were other values in the order of the two family sessions. If family art therapy came first, much material was projected through the art productions that could be further explored in the conjoint family verbal therapy session that followed. If the sequence was reversed, the art therapy provided closure, giving the family an opportunity to express in their pictures emotions stirred in the preceding therapeutic hour. Family members often remarked that this additional hour filled an urgent need.

THE ROLE OF THE ART THERAPIST

The part played by the art therapist depends in the first place on the interest in and understanding of the power of the creative experience by those who lead the institution where the art therapist works. That interest and understanding often determine whether or not an art therapist is hired. But it does not end there. The chief may leave, and upon his departure the whole therapeutic program may be completely changed. It would be sad if the art therapist were totally dependent on the support of the key person. He has to establish his own place as a clinician or a researcher. If the art therapist knows where he fits and what he can contribute, the battle for acceptance is half won.

I found a variety of staff responses, from enthusiastic endorsement, through intrigued but cautious interest, to skepticism and open reluctance to accept a therapeutic technique so far removed from the rigidly circumscribed medical tradition.

Despite the richness of my experience and the rewarding recognition accorded me, I would not be sincere if I described my long years in art therapy as a utopian rose garden.* Nevertheless, though there were thorns, they were fewer by far than the blossoms.

---

*This allusion to a rose garden came to my mind in connection with the book by Hannah Green, *I Never Promised You a Rose Garden.*⁷

Among today's many new therapeutic procedures, art therapy has gained a respected position, but there are still many skeptics. Most painful for the art therapist is to work in surroundings where his work is tolerated with a certain condescension as possibly useful but something one really could do very well without. In the words of someone whose name was impossible to trace, "There is nothing more intolerable than being tolerated."

How does one overcome rejection, doubt, resistance and anxiety on the part of the staff in a therapeutic community? Certainly not through speeches and demonstrations of therapeutic success nor by distributing literature that no one reads. There is, however, one avenue that rarely fails: personal experience. Staff response tends to be similar to that of families initially reluctant to engage in a procedure so alien to them as expression through images. At first family members talk about their lack of skills, liken art therapy to returning to kindergarten, and repeat insistently, "You will never make an artist out of me." This changes quickly, however, when they discover the meaning revealed by their first group of pictures.

The staff goes through the same shift of attitude. Those who themselves undergo the same experience with the expressive use of art as the patients do are usually won over much more easily and discover that adding a new tool to their therapeutic armamentarium does not diminish their professional prestige.

It is essential that the art therapist teach his fellow staff members what it feels like to express oneself through art. The most convincing lecture illustrated with impressive case material is far less successful than is personal experience.

A workshop or series of workshops in which as many staff members as possible, from the highest to the lowest in the hierarchy, participate in the actual artwork is invaluable at the start of an art therapy program. When the interest has been aroused, as it rarely fails to be, relevant clinical material should be presented, selected reading should be recommended, and above all, staff members should be invited to participate as cotherapists in the family art procedures.

When family art therapy serves as an adjunct to verbal family therapy, it is most important for the art therapist to observe (when a one-way mirror is available) as many of the other therapeutic sessions held with the family as possible. He should also take part in postsession discussions and study notes written by the other therapists as well as make his own notes available to them. This contributes to the cohesion of both approaches.

Where no other forms of treatment are used with the family, the psychiatrist-cotherapist and the art therapist conduct therapy independently. However, in both approaches, primary and adjunctive, as well as in family art evaluations, it is most desirable to invite all staff members who are part of the milieu, even if they are not directly involved in family therapy, to observe the art sessions. This practice not only adds to the acceptance of art therapy but also enables the staff to contribute to the understanding of material obtained in the family art sessions.

THE COTHERAPISTS IN FAMILY ART THERAPY

Because it is so taxing to work with disturbed families, it is most desirable to work with a cotherapist, just as it is in verbal conjoint family therapy. The cotherapists provide support to each other and can later share and discuss their reactions to what was going on in the family. In family art therapy, when so many different activities are going on at one time, the role of the cotherapist is even more important.

The cotherapist is usually the psychiatrist responsible for the family treatment or any other staff member involved in the treatment program for the family. In the art therapy sessions the roles of the art therapist and the cotherapist are equal. There is no special leadership of one or the other; a suggestion for active work may come from either.

The style in conducting family art therapy depends largely upon the therapists' preferences, personalities and theoretical views of family therapy. At times the therapists may, like the family, express their own experiences pictorially. Such active participation of therapists in the session has proved to be helpful with certain types of families and in particular cases.

The family with paranoid tendencies is apt to become uncomfortable about being watched by the therapists while working at the easels, and their suspicion that they are being spied upon or controlled may thus be reinforced. But the open expression of the therapists' feelings in pictures portraying their own immediate reactions prompts the family to see more commitment by the therapists. They cease to be the silent impersonal observers who scrutinize and watch. They become part of the family's experience, persons who express their feelings, just as they encourage the family to do. Therefore they can be trusted more easily.

The therapists' active participation may also alleviate the apathy and withdrawal of the family group. The family is encouraged and stimulated by such a supportive gesture, and this results in more activity by the family and in the loosening of some of their defenses.[8] But how do the therapists feel in this unorthodox situation?

It may be somewhat easier for the art therapist trained in the use of art as a vehicle of expression to produce his own artwork during a session than it is for the psychiatrist, psychologist or social worker, whose mode of communication remains mainly verbal. He may go through feelings similar to those of the family when faced with the blank sheet of paper: the usual doubts about his skill and about how much he is willing to reveal. Thus such participation is possible only when it is done on impulse, is prompted by the therapist's own needs, and is carried out with complete sincerity. The basis of every therapeutic relationship, of course, is honesty. But this procedure requires more than honesty; it calls for the courage to expose oneself without the restriction of fears about how the family will respond to this.

Such total commitment by therapists in trying to experience with the family feelings difficult to express and their complete immersion in what is happening at the moment usually evoke a positive response.

None of my cotherapists who participated actively in artwork with families were artists; their drawing occasionally or regularly was spontaneous and unplanned. Yet the heightened trust of these families convinced us that this was what had been needed at that point.

An occurrence in the course of our work with Mr. and Mrs. Jones and their twenty-three-year-old daughter Sally serves as an example.

Sally was an intelligent, attractive girl whose behavior and appearance did not at first reveal much psychopathology. But her history disclosed recurrent hospitalizations resulting from a wide range of symptoms, including hypomania, overuse of marijuana, suicidal gestures, self-mutilation, delusions and hallucinations.

When seen in family art therapy, Sally politely refused to take part at a deep level; she would comply superficially by quickly drawing empty, vague pictures. Her standard response to any suggestion that she look for some meaning in her or her parents' art productions was, "I would rather not talk about it."

Sally believed that the only way to deal with troubling thoughts was to put the lid on them. But the thoughts remained; she told only her parents and her two younger sisters about her paranoid delusions of being constantly spied upon by staff and patients. Her power over her family was so strong that she successfully coerced them into keeping her delusions a secret. This, of course, interfered seriously with the treatment, immobilizing everyone. The family hinted that something was going on, but somehow they were caught up in the system, even if they were aware of Sally's distortions.

The therapy sessions were unproductive. As a counterpart to Sally's sparse, negligently executed, barely visible sketches, the other family members drew carefully preplanned pictures. The parents presented an intellectually rationalized and censored pictorial version of the reason for Sally's difficulties, assigning blame for her condition to one person or another. Her sisters abstained from any expressive commitment; they drew mostly abstract designs, drip-paint pictures, or bland fruit and flower pieces.

Sally's delusions about the therapists' magic power to control their minds weighed heavily on all of them. The family members were distrustful and hypersensitive to any comments the therapists made. In turn the therapists were virtually helpless; they tried in vain to reach the family, to focus on the experience actually shared in the therapeutic hour. Two measures were then taken to ease the severe tensions: One was to have the family members decide when and what they wished to draw during the hour, and the other was to have the therapists draw the chosen topic along with the family.

These decisions were announced to the family at the end of a session; the therapists felt unsure what the family's and their own reaction would be. It so happened that in that hour there was friction between the two therapists. One began to comment before the other had finished expressing his own thoughts, to the extreme annoyance of the one who was interrupted. This disagreement delighted the family. Mrs. Jones said jokingly that maybe they should go out and let the therapists finish their squabble alone, and even Sally laughed wholeheartedly.

This incident proved to be useful to the family. They could see the therapists as real people, not as stuffed figures who never disagreed or experienced irritation.

It was encouraging when, at the next meeting, Sally was the one to suggest a topic for the family and the therapists to draw. The subject she chose was quite personal: how each member of the group saw Sally's future fate.

This seemed to be a turning point for Sally. She became vividly interested in the therapists' pictures, and in some of them found a reflection of her own feelings. Although her own art productions remained meager and controlled, they now became more related to the problem under discussion. Her parents' pictures continued to be intellectualized, but the whole family seemed to come out from under the spell of the "family secret" and was able to work more productively in therapy.

As in any other therapeutic situation where two or more therapists work together, in family art therapy the relationship between the cotherapists is important and if not adequately clarified may impair treatment. This particular situation is even more ambiguous than that in verbal psychotherapy. Not only may personalities clash, but the different backgrounds and roles of the cotherapists may create problems. The treating physician may be seen by the family as the person in supreme authority, responsible for the entire treatment, prescribing drugs, signing passes, etc. The role of the art therapist is less clear to them. Nevertheless, I cannot recall any lack of confidence or respect toward me on the part of the families. In large measure I attribute this to the peculiar power of art, which, when it enters the sphere of communication, seems to obliterate all differences.

What goes on between the two therapists is more complicated. In any therapy that involves cotherapists, the more aggressive of the pair often tends to monopolize the session, provoking a defensive reaction from the other. The resulting tensions reflect in one way or another on the treatment process.

It is no novelty for therapists in group discussion to openly discuss their conflicting feelings. The degree of the openness depends on both the theoretical views and the personal style of the therapists. When the therapists are active participants in the process of drawing in a group, as was seen in the example just described, the graphic expression of their feelings regarding the situation and each other may be explored to whatever degree seems desirable at a particular point. The experience can in itself be cathartic, thus releasing tensions between therapists. This undoubtedly has a favorable impact on the family group. Furthermore, the therapists can later return to their pictures and explore issues at a more intimate level.

Another problem arises when the patient is seen individually by one of the therapists. This can produce competition between the cotherapists for the patient, as well as a dilemma about the confidentiality of the material that comes up in individual therapy. Should this material be brought up openly in the family group?

There is no general solution on how to deal with such a situation. Theoretically it is best to make clear to patients that complete confidentiality is not to be expected when the family is being treated as an entity. In practice, though, this may not be possible. The complications of combining individual, couple, and family therapy are well known, but here I emphasize an aspect of this problem that is very specific to the graphic as opposed to the verbal form of expression. Pictures done in the family group may at times bring to the surface subjects barely touched upon earlier in the verbal individual session. It is most frustrating for the therapist not to feel free to use this material in the context of the current experience with the whole family.

An example of how such an inhibition may not only interfere with a therapist's effectiveness but also may affect the cotherapist who knows nothing about what went on in the individual session is provided by a family art session with the Proffin family.

Participating were Mr. and Mrs. Proffin, their sixteen-year-old son Michael, and their eleven-year-old daughter Samantha.

Michael, the identified patient, presented a number of emotional problems, which were manifested in his behavior and impaired his functioning. He was a heavy user of drugs and alcohol, frequently ran away, and had a court record. Also, he had previously been hospitalized as the result of a drug overdose.

Michael was afraid to express any aggressive feelings. He also had a great fear of intimacy when he was alone with a therapist, though at the same time he was starved for affection. He was seen in individual psychotherapy and with his parents in verbal conjoint therapy.

Michael, his parents and his sister participated in evaluative art procedures lasting two sessions. The decision to extend the customary single evaluation session to two meetings was made because the family responded so well to the art technique.* Their usual withdrawal and depression soon gave way to real involvement of all family members. They talked vividly about their pictures, and this brought to light interesting material not readily available in their psychotherapeutic sessions.

Samantha's participation was a great asset. Her brightness and charm, her perceptive observations, unusual for a child her age, and her remarks on what she saw in the family pictures con-

---

*The family art evaluation session is not limited in time; the required six procedures are designed to be completed in one meeting taking a minimum of one and one-half hours. However, the session is extended to two meetings if there is a special reason for doing so: the family's unusually productive response or, to the contrary, its slowness and resistance, or a time limitation due to work or school obligations of family members.

tributed to a large degree to the fruitfulness of the first part of the art evaluation session and made the therapists feel comfortable.

The second meeting, four days later, started rather graciously. Mrs. Proffin expressed her pleasure at coming back and claimed to have arrived at an understanding of many things through the pictures. She also emphasized that she had never before seen her husband draw and that she had discovered new aspects of him. Mr. Proffin returned the compliment, praising his wife's skills in many areas. They both admired Michael's talents. To give an example of Samantha's perceptiveness, I quote her observation: "It seems that everyone is bragging about everyone else!" Mr. Proffin remarked that this was characteristic of the family.

But as the session advanced, the family became increasingly depressed. The therapists experienced a rising discomfort and felt somehow out of tune with each other, as if each were waiting for the other to make an interpretation or to encourage the family to explore any more expressive pictures. This uneasiness was particularly strong when one of Michael's pictures was discussed.

Figure 1.

The picture represents a wagon entering a covered bridge over a deep ravine (Fig. 1). Michael saw it as "very rural: a farmer going away to the market to avoid all the hubbub of the city." For a while the dangerous location of the bridge was discussed, and mother questioned why Michael drew the farmer entering the bridge instead of getting out of the bridge.

The psychiatrist tried to relate this to the way Michael saw himself at that point. Michael "happened to disagree"; he thought he knew what everybody was thinking about. Mostly he talked about the peace and quiet of the country.

Both therapists continued to make weak, unsuccessful attempts to help Michael connect his reluctance to leave the shelter of the covered bridge with his mixed feelings about breaking the tie with his parents. Actually the scene he depicted is arid and deserted rather than peaceful and quiet. But somehow all the symbolic richness of this material was fading out, leaving the family depressed and the therapists frustrated and annoyed with each other.

After the session was over, the therapists got together to try to clarify what had happened. It was only then that I learned that in the individual therapy hour immediately preceding the art evaluation session, Michael had spoken of a nightmare about stealing a car. The car went faster and faster until it "took off" and Michael fell to the ground terrified. This had been discussed in terms of his feelings of insecurity, his difficulty in "taking off," detaching himself from the mother-car.

Another picture done by Michael at this session, "Mother and Child" (Fig. 2), was even more eloquent. He started it with the help of a scribble.* Michael described it as a "baby inside of the mother's stomach, just starting to form." Samantha, with her usual perceptiveness, commented on how sad the mother looks. Even though the mother's mouth is turned down, Michael did

---

*The scribble technique, which is more fully described in Chapter IV, consists of a picture developed from a freely drawn broad scribble. The shapes of the intercrossing lines bring forth associations that become the subject of the picture. Such scribble pictures can be drawn individually or jointly by all the family members.

not see it as showing the mother's sadness about letting the baby go; he kept talking about the happiness of both the mother and the baby "starting a new life." But at the same time he spoke regretfully of how comfortable the baby was there, close to its mother.

Figure 2.

The psychiatrist felt that the pictures were a continuation of the individual session with him, of the theme of Michael's and his mother's inability to separate from each other, and Michael's denial of this problem. But he did not feel free to bring these ideas up with the family. He projected his frustration onto me, annoyed that I did not make enough use of this valuable material. In the meantime I felt confused about what was going on and unsure about how far I should go in view of the psychiatrist's restraint. Because of the therapists' discomfort, all this important material was left almost entirely unexplored.

I have discussed both of these cases to exemplify the intricacies of the cotherapists' relationships mainly as a warning to those who engage in family art therapy. It is a serious matter, which, if not dealt with, can lead to complete failure in the exploration of important material.

CHAPTER III

THE FAMILY ART SESSION

I N BOTH PROCEDURES, therapeutic and evaluative, the physical setting is similar: a room large enough to accommodate a folding floor easel for each family member, and chairs for family and therapists. The choice of easels and chairs is left to the family members. It is advisable, if space permits, to provide one more easel than the number of persons participating. The location of the easel that remains unoccupied may indicate a family member's desire either to isolate himself or to be closely connected with another family member.

The easels are placed in a semicircle not only to allow the family members to work on their own without interference, but also to allow each one to see what the others are doing. Despite that openness, family members seldom copy from each other. If they do, it provides valuable clues about their relationship.

The easels are adjustable, but we do not offer to help younger children to fix them at the height they need. We leave it to the parents to make any rearrangements needed by their children, thus providing them the opportunity to reproduce the circumstances of their daily life. Only if parents pay no attention to the children's needs do we come to the rescue. The parents' behavior in such a situation produces valuable material that can be further used therapeutically.

Family art therapy requires a space adequately equipped for handling paint and clay: available water, space for storage of a variety of art materials, tables or sculpture stands for working in clay, and an uncarpeted floor. This, of course, is the ideal setting, but we have successfully conducted family art therapy in much less favorable environments.

For research purposes it is highly desirable to have a tape recorder available and, if possible, a video recording machine behind a one-way mirror. The one-way mirror is especially useful in art evaluations. It provides an opportunity for the whole team involved in work with a family to see the family in action, to acquire first-hand experience of the family dynamics, and to share more amply their impressions in a postsession discussion. In some instances, a family member may be invited to come behind the mirror, as has been done by Minuchin.[9]

I have not done this myself but can see in it valuable possibilities for the exploration of family members' more objective reactions to what is going on during their absence in their families. The playing back of video tape of the session to the family also has interesting possibilities. I would, however, advise that it be done with caution as it might be a shattering experience for the family.

In family art therapy sessions easy-to-use art materials—square semihard pastels, tempera paints, eighteen by twenty-four-inch drawing paper and terra-cotta clay—are made readily available to the family but are only gradually introduced; later, the family is free to use whatever they wish.

In family art evaluations the art materials are limited to a box of square pastels for each participant. We do this for a twofold reason. First, we want to obtain material as uniform as possible for research purposes; second, because we give the family a number of tasks to be done in one session, we provide an art medium that is easy to use, gives quick results, and is equally accessible to all regardless of their skills or experience in the use of graphic materials. Family art evaluations can therefore be conducted in any interview room that provides the necessary space. The equipment can be set up in a few minutes and the room quickly cleared after the session is over.

Even when recording equipment is used, note taking and abstract writing remain an important part of the work, even though they may become cumbersome and time-consuming endeavors because of the therapist's exhaustion following an intensive session with a family. However, it is most important to write up one's observations as soon after the session as possible, especially on the nonverbal communications between family members. Note taking during the session is a matter of personal preference. I myself feel that intensive note taking during the therapy session distracts my attention from what is going on. It is somewhat different in the evaluation session, where a number of tasks are required and notes are easier to take during the periods of the family's active work while performing these tasks. Last but not least, it is imperative to record one's personal impressions and subjective reactions during the session.

The very abundance of material obtained in these sessions may make it difficult to sort out and describe its most important aspects. One is apt to get drowned in details and to produce voluminous notes in which the focal conflict may be completely lost and which have little chance of being read even by interested people engaged in work with the family.

While writing this book I have at times been faced with paying for my early sins: occasional lack of adequate notes, dates and identifications of pictures and sculptures. While one is immersed in the intensity of the sessions, details are felt to be engraved in one's memory forever. But this is not so. One sees more and more families; the collection of pictures and sculptures grows, and even if they evoke the original emotions, many details escape memory. To recount my experiences to others, I spent innumerable frustrating hours trying to find dates, quotations and titles. An outline to be followed when composing one's notes is a great help. (See Appendix I.)

Evaluative and therapeutic sessions differ in length. The family art therapy session, like any other therapeutic session, is strictly defined, but is extended from the customary sixty minutes to ninety minutes because of the time consumed by drawing, painting or sculpting. Otherwise, there is no particular structure; family members are left free to use as much time as they want for active work and to discuss their work when they wish, while engaged in the artwork or after having finished it. They are not urged to "produce" but when an important issue is spoken of in the session or when, on the contrary, the family evades such an issue, the therapist may suggest that they express it in the form of a picture. Such a picture or set of pictures by different family members may serve as a subject of discussion for several sessions, until the problems or feelings brought to the surface have been adequately explored.

This is an important point. Picture making may become a defensive maneuver to evade feelings that are painful or difficult to touch upon. Therefore, at times therapists even have to discourage art activity when it is being used defensively.

MEETING THE FAMILY

As was stated earlier, the inclusion of the family in the art therapy sessions began without having been planned. Since family members took part mainly at their own initiative, there was at first no problem about drawing them into art activity. When family art therapy and family art evaluation became an official part of the clinical program, the situation changed. We had to expect and deal with the families' resistance and anxiety when they were confronted with easels and art materials and the prospect of using them.

Believing that an elaborate explanation of methods and goals would probably arouse even more anxiety, we decided that it would be best to merely inform the families that they would have a session during which some drawing would be done. In most cases the patients and their families had never seen me before and I knew little or nothing about them.

At the sight of the room equipped with easels, papers, paints and pastels, family members typically say things like, "I don't know how to draw a straight line," "You will never make an artist out of me," etc.

The art therapist must be reassuring but firm. The family is told that their artistic skills or talent are not being examined but rather that the easy art media are offered in order for them to express themselves or to communicate with each other in another way. Immediately it is added that the best way to understand the procedure is to start right away and see for themselves what it is all about. The art therapist demonstrates in a couple of strokes the use of the broad side and of the angular end of the pastels and invites the family to do a picture of whatever they wish or whatever comes to mind. Usually, except for younger children, the family members rather reluctantly get up and approach the easels.

What is remarkable is that after the first picture has been drawn by each of them, we rarely hear further protestations of inability or of unwillingness to continue. Seeing that one person's picture conveys a message that arouses the interest of other family members usually dissolves the initial resistance. Also, the therapists' acceptance of the family's art products, regardless of their artistic merit, makes them feel at ease and willing to continue. They quickly realize that even a few clumsy lines can say quite a lot.

Families who are going to be seen in family art therapy as the primary mode of treatment are told even less. They are seen in a preadmission session in a room already equipped with all that is necessary for drawing.

We see on most faces a puzzled expression. If a question is asked about the art equipment, we answer much as we do the families with whom art is to be used as an adjunctive therapeutic or evaluative procedure. When in the course of the session a subject comes up that is hard to express in words, we suggest it be represented pictorially. We hear some protestations but far fewer than I at first expected. We then tell the families that this is the way we are going to work with them. Although the protestations regarding lack of skill, etc., continue, no one has withdrawn after hearing this announcement. It would seem that the peculiar nature of the art experience helps break down self-consciousness, distrust and caution.

Let us not deceive ourselves, however; as in any other therapy, resistance may come later, not so much to the graphic method as to the therapeutic process as a whole.

When working with families, the art therapist may be caught in the web of many situations. There are many opportunities to be manipulated into an entanglement with a particularly demanding and aggressive family member. Request for technical help may constitute an effective ruse to monopolize the art therapist's attention. His very capacities make him an easier target than the cotherapist, who is not equipped with the same skills. The art therapist must be on constant watch to be giving but not to be possessed.

Another pitfall to be avoided is that of succumbing to his enchantment with a talented family member. This may become a difficult task. When constantly faced with products of a rather low artistic quality, it is a joy to occasionally see something beautiful. On the other hand, crude and naive markings may bring to light a poignant truth and thus be more gratifying from the therapeutic point of view than the "good" picture. Hardest to take are emptiness and stereotypy, so difficult at times to break away from.

Outstanding talent of one of the family members is also apt to increase the self-consciousness and therefore the resistance of the less skilled participants. In such event the art therapist must give support and convey his belief that their limited use of graphic expression can be as valuable therapeutically as can the most skillful picture. If the art therapist does not sincerely believe this, however, his reassurances will be empty, leaving the family members with their original discomfort and embarrassment.

On the other hand, successful art expression by one family member may have a positive aspect. Time and again we hear such exclamations as "I never knew Daddy could draw!" or evidence that skillful artwork has revealed a facet of someone that had not been known to the other members of the family. This happens mostly between parents.

The effects of unequal skills and experience in a group so different in personality and age are endlessly varied. They range from ego-building, supportive behavior to destructive mockery on the part of family members; these attitudes provide valuable insight into family relations and dynamics. This is one of the factors that, despite all the advantages of graphic expression in family therapy, make for special difficulties that require solid experience and special sensitivity on the part of the art therapist.

DISCUSSION OF ART PRODUCTS

In discussing the family art products with the family, we follow, up to a point, the general principles of group art therapy. The pictures are not put up for display but upon completion are visible on the easels. Discussion may take place spontaneously, stimulated by a family member's remark or question; this of course is best. At other times the therapist must offer encouragement to an apathetic and withdrawn family. Direct questions may make them withdraw further or may evoke superficial, evasive answers. I have found it better to invite the family to say whether there is anything in each other's pictures they would like to know more about, or if something is blatantly filled with symbolic meaning and nobody reacts to it, I suggest that the family members focus on this particular picture, expressing my own interest and indicating that I wonder about the family's reaction to it. Interpretations by the therapists are made only when the family is well engaged in therapy, but even then we try to hear the family's reactions to their and others' pictures first.

Younger children participating in family art sessions are, as is to be expected, the most free in drawing and need little encouragement. They usually draw spontaneously, and their pictures often express feelings far beyond their awareness. When it comes to translating them into words and bringing them to a more conscious level, however, young children may become completely unable to respond to the family's or therapists' efforts to get them to talk about the sometimes cryptic messages of their pictures. It usually helps in such cases to ask them to tell a story about their pictures. Children can almost always fantasize a story that may carry a poignant symbolic message. An example of this can be seen in a scribble picture drawn by ten-year-old Lilian in a family art evaluation session.

Lilian was faced with the difficult problem of forming a relationship with a new father. Her mother had remarried a year earlier; her stepfather, Mr. Brennan, was an alcoholic in treatment in a halfway house. Lilian, the only child, was being brought up by her mother in a fatherless home.

The parents and Lilian participated in a family art evaluation session in which the intricate relationship of these three persons was vividly displayed. Lilian seemed to be a tool used by Mr. Brennan to preserve his precarious marriage. Mrs. Brennan seemed tired of the struggle to reconcile her views with those of her husband about the world in general and about Lilian's upbringing. Her efforts to understand him were not successful.

During the family art evaluation Mr. Brennan's long moralistic speeches were almost impossible to follow and seemed to indicate thought disorder. He sat close to Lilian and carried on constant private exchanges with her. Lilian seemed to accept this closeness and to be under the spell of the intensity of her stepfather's attention. There was a complete split between Mr. Brennan and Lilian on one side and Mrs. Brennan on the other.

At that point Mr. Brennan's behavior did not seem sexually seductive. Rather, he appeared to be trying to recruit an ally who would help him maintain his marital relationship. He seemed to see Lilian more as filling his own needs than as a child in need of a father. Lilian's scribble picture "Baby Day" (Fig. 3) consists of entangled lines in green, orange and brown forming an unrecog-

Figure 3.

nizable shape. But the title intrigued us. We asked her to tell
us a story about it.

> It is like a baby carriage. . . . A man and a wife had a baby. The
> man was nervous. His wife asked him to get a baby carriage. He
> forgot what to get and the salesman gave him a rocking chair. . . .
> When they put the baby in it, the first word he said was "Baby Day."

The story threw some light on Lilian's preoccupation with being
"born" to a new father and on the joy of its being *her* day, "Baby
Day."

But there was another side to it. The father's "nervousness"
made him "forget" what was really needed by a newborn baby.
Instead of the baby carriage, he bought a rocking chair. His
treatment of her was as unsuitable as is a rocking chair for a newborn baby, which was as confusing to her as were the entangled
lines of her picture.

This father-stepdaughter relationship was fraught with complications that went far beyond Lilian's story, but her fantasy
vividly reflected her confusion and discomfort.

The art therapist is faced at times with another problem: the
verbose family. It is especially difficult to deal with such families
in the family art evaluation, when a number of tasks have to be
completed and discussed in a limited time. Of course, one must
distinguish between the family that becomes seriously emotionally
involved in the discussion of pictures and the family whose members express their anxiety or resistance by giggling, making
private jokes or endlessly reciting their mutual grievances.

The emotionally expressive family presents particular problems for the art therapist in the family art evaluation. He is
reluctant to cut off the flow of valuable material because the
temptation to fully explore it is great. As frustrating and delicate
as the task may be, he must remind the family about the number
of drawings to be done in the evaluative session and suggest that
they discuss the pictures further in the verbal family therapy
sessions. The permanence of the pictorial material permits a
more vivid revival of the experience than when one attempts to
carry over a discussion from one verbal therapy session to another.
This aspect of artwork is particularly valuable when working with

families of schizophrenics, whose experience is fragmented, easily disrupted or amorphous.

Another solution when the family is overly productive in a single art evaluation session is to divide it into two sessions. This is not recommended, however, unless the session goes far beyond the available time. The tasks have been placed in a particular sequence for specific purposes, and it is important to maintain their juxtaposition if possible. (This subject will be further explained in Chapter VII.) Coordinating the family's and the therapists' time for the other half of the session may also present difficulties, but in my experience families were always quite willing, at times even eager, to return to continue the tasks of the evaluation. When a family is not engaged in the therapeutic program and the family art evaluation is the only encounter with all its members present, there may be an overriding reason to plan a second postevaluation session that provides more opportunity to explore in greater depth with the family the obtained material.

One must be firm with families who disrupt the session either with constant bickering or with an irrelevant flow of words. The family should be made aware immediately that this behavior annoys the therapists; eventually such maneuvers should be explored as one of the patterns of family behavior.

If family members do not spontaneously write titles on their pictures, they are asked to do so. They are also asked to sign and date their art products.

The title seems to give some kind of closure to what is graphically expressed; I have found it useful and revealing in many ways. The title may add meaning to a crude design; it may have no connection with what has been drawn; it may have an idiosyncratic connection with the picture; or it may be quite literal, adding nothing. The variety of titles used by different family members, when they have been asked to draw a picture of their family, serves a useful purpose. Titles such as "Family," "My Family," "A Happy Family," "A Mixed-up Family," "People," and "Us" may become the springboard for an animated discussion of how differently the family is viewed by its individual members.

The size, importance and placement of the signature is also

indicative of self-perception; at times it is so grandiose that it dominates the picture.

As for the date, its correctness or incorrectness indicates the subject's awareness of time. Sometimes a wrong date that seems to have no special significance at the time may later turn out to be linked with a crucial past event. Dating all pictures also serves the purpose of helping to keep them in chronological order for use in research, writing or clinical presentations.

CHAPTER IV

FAMILY ART THERAPY AS A TECHNIQUE ADJUNCTIVE TO VERBAL FAMILY THERAPY

THIS CHAPTER will focus on family art therapy as an adjunctive technique conducted in parallel with conjoint family therapy and on the relationship between these two modes of treatment.

In our initial work at the National Institute of Mental Health we saw families in six sessions. From this we could judge whether there was promise of therapeutic usefulness. We would then either discontinue the family art sessions or continue them concomitant with conjoint verbal family therapy. Even if the family was not further seen in family art therapy, these six sessions provided valuable observations on family dynamics as well as material for research.

As this new therapeutic technique developed, many changes were necessary. We had nothing to guide us but our experience.

At first the members of the family were seen individually for one or two sessions to establish rapport with me; the patient, who had previously been seen alone in individual art therapy, had already established rapport with me.

Then we tried a number of additional configurations. Family members were seen in subgroups, such as parents as a couple; parents with the identified patient; parents with "well" siblings; well siblings as a group both with and without the identified patient; and finally the whole family group together. Work with these subgroups provided enlightening material on the differences in their art productions and behavior, depending on who the participants were, but clinically it had its drawbacks. The switch from these subgroups to the whole family was at times resented and seen as an invasion by others of their relationship with me. As a result, members of the family became less responsive and at times withdrew.

After a time we established the practice of seeing the entire family group together from the start. However, the arrangement was flexible and, as described in Chapter II, individuals were at times scheduled for additional sessions alone with me. The following experiences illustrate some of the circumstances that dictated such a decision.

The Williams family was one of the first to be invited to participate in the art therapy sessions. The family consisted of Mr. and Mrs. Williams, ages fifty-four and fifty, their daughter Peggy (the hospitalized family member), age twenty-four, and their son Philip. Peggy's diagnosis was schizophrenic reaction, chronic undifferentiated type, with paranoid features. In Chapter I, I described the art session with Peggy and Philip as one of the experiences that triggered our interest in this new approach.

After several art therapy sessions with the Williamses, it was necessary to see Mrs. Williams in individual sessions for a while. In the family art sessions her resistance had been manifested by her constant complaints about her lack of talent and her inability to draw anything, or by her stubborn withdrawal from any active participation, accompanied occasionally by selective deafness. Furthermore, Peggy never missed a chance to attack her mother with angry outbursts at almost anything she said. Mr. Williams assumed a superficial head-of-the-family role, but actually remained remote and did not interfere in the frequent crises between mother and daughter, which would leave Mrs. Williams terrified and with only one thought: how to get away from it all as quickly as possible. She accepted eagerly the suggestion of a few individual sessions, which would allow her to become familiar with the art media. In fact, however, her willingness seemed to be caused mostly by her relief at not having to be exposed to her daughter's attacks.

Peggy, who had had individual art therapy for ten months before the family's participation, indirectly showed her resentment
at sharing me with her mother by constantly intruding during her
mother's early sessions. She declared that her mother was not
interested, saying, "My mother does not come here for drawing;
she comes to be with me—at least I hope so." She also attacked
me in much the same way that she had attacked her mother during the family art sessions, using insulting words and adroitly
aiming at what hurt most.

Freed of Peggy's intense, possessively aggressive presence, Mrs.
Williams gradually became more relaxed during her five individual sessions. She also was less preoccupied by her lack of
skill and even found some enjoyment in creating her naively
primitive pictures when she realized that they were accepted without criticism. She was very talkative, and much of the patient's
and the family's history came up during these sessions.

According to our plans the family was again to be seen together when Mrs. Williams had become more familiar with the
art media and more accepting of art therapy. But when we resumed the family sessions, Mr. Williams started to show resistance
and maneuvered his way out of the sessions with excuses of professional duties or physical illness. We were not too insistent on
his participation, feeling that one of the core problems was the
complex symbiotic relationship between mother and daughter.
This in turn seemed to stem from similar ties Mrs. Williams had
had with her own deceased mother. Therefore, work with mother
and daughter was most important in this case.

When we announced to Mrs. Williams that work would be
resumed with her and Peggy, we were impressed by her reaction.
She used the same arguments and took the same negative view of
the usefulness of art therapy for herself that Peggy had voiced at
the time of her mother's individual sessions. "It doesn't do me
any good; I don't like it," she said, echoing Peggy's earlier predic-
tions.

Despite Mrs. Williams' renewed reluctance, the mother-daughter sessions were resumed; Peggy and her mother had thirty joint

sessions. Their pictures and behavior provided a great deal of material demonstrating some of the intricacies of work with families of schizophrenics and of thought processes in schizophrenia that seemed here to be similar in parent and offspring and that will be further described in a later chapter.

In another family the identified patient, Robert, was the twenty-eight-year-old schizophrenic son of a highly verbal couple who were very involved in their marital problems. As was otherwise usual in this family, during art therapy sessions Robert became completely isolated from his parents, who practically ignored his presence. I too was drawn into this pattern and was initially so overwhelmed by the fascinatingly rich, though often obscure or overintellectualized, material the parents produced, that it was hard for me to give enough attention to the son.

Robert tried to focus some attention on himself by attacking the parents verbally. He got even with me by refusing to participate in the family art activities.

Robert was then later seen separately in addition to the family sessions, and gradually we established rapport. Not only did he take a more active part in the family art therapy sessions, but I had also developed an interest in him that I could comfortably maintain despite the parents' continuing pressure for my attention.

Mr. Richards, the father in still another family, kept saying he had no talent in comparison with his quite gifted wife. He used this as an excuse for his refusal to participate in the family art therapy sessions. A few individual art sessions were held with him to help him understand that talent was not crucial in expressing one's feelings and his resistance was overcome.

In another case, Mrs. Kiston, the mother of a nineteen-year-old college student hospitalized with a diagnosis of adjustment reaction to adolescence, refused to take active part in the family sessions, though she made no objection to being present. This made her husband and son, the patient, tense and angry. They were extremely irritated by her failure to participate actively. Mrs. Kiston was a rigid, domineering person who assumed the role of a defenseless, fragile woman seeking protection from her husband.

When an individual session was suggested to her, she asked, "Why was I singled out?" She was told, "You singled yourself out."

Consequently she was seen in several individual sessions. In one of them a scribble picture was suggested to her in the hope that this technique would help her loosen up (the scribble technique is described later in this chapter). As we can see in Figure 4, she remained quite rigid and did not even attempt to develop her initial scribble into a picture. Despite this, however, it served a useful purpose. She called the picture "A Woman Made of Wire." When asked for further comment, she said, "What more can one say of a woman made of wire?" She claimed having always been concerned with the physical well-being of her children, but she was probably unable to give them much more warmth

Figure 4.

than the surrogate "wire mother" used by Harlow and Zimmerman[11] in their experiments with baby monkeys. This rigid representation was a tacit acknowledgment of a view of herself that she had been afraid to recognize and reveal.

In the next art therapy session, when the whole family was seen again, the father developed from his scribble a witchlike portrait of "Madame Defarge Without Knitting Needles" (Fig. 5). He did not make any immediate comments, but the family's tense silence led us to believe that they, like us, saw in this picture a hostile representation of his wife.

When both parents' pictures were discussed at the end of the art therapy session, the mother was able to realize that her cool

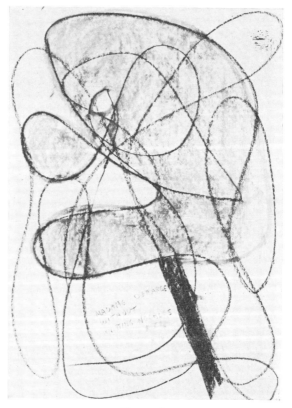

Figure 5.

detachment made her husband furious. In the next family verbal psychotherapy session, the mother's resistance to participate in family art therapy was further discussed; the therapists pointed out how her behavior affected the rest of the family, how angry she made them, and how she really controlled them in this and other situations. This art therapy experience was seen by the psychiatrist as a turning point in the family's psychotherapy; Mrs. Kiston's defenses had been loosened to the point where she could fruitfully participate in the group.

In the family art therapy sessions we were not only discovering dynamics specific to families with identified patients belonging to different diagnostic groups, but we were also becoming aware of how much we could achieve therapeutically and how our work tied in with and contributed to other therapeutic procedures. Since the cotherapist in family art therapy was one of the two therapists conducting conjoint verbal family therapy, the two sessions were closely connected; quite frequently one was a continuation of the other.

Strong negative feelings between family members incessantly denied in words were coming to the surface in pictures and sculptures with undeniable clarity. Furthermore, these expressions were also being somehow accepted by both the one who produced the artwork and the one who was the butt of his feelings without leaving the former with too much guilt and the latter too overwhelmed and crushed.

The art therapy sessions were totally nondirective; the choice of medium and subject was left to the family members. We were gradually introducing the families to pastels, tempera paints and terra-cotta clay.

The use of the scribble as the start of a picture was encouraged when the family members had a tendency to draw stereotyped, preplanned pictures. The scribble also proved to be outstandingly effective in uncovering feelings otherwise denied or repressed.

The scribble technique is well known to art therapists but may be less familiar to readers from other fields. Basically the scribble is a creatively stimulative technique that helps the individual to escape from self-imposed standards, whether imitative or stereotyped. Loosening free and rhythmic arm motions in the air are a preparation for the drawing of broad free-flowing lines on the paper.

While drawing the scribble, the individual is asked to do it with closed eyes in order not to guide and control the lines and shapes he draws. The lines and shapes obtained in this way serve as stimuli to associations that lead to the choice of the subject for a picture.

In developing the picture, the individual may add as many lines as he wishes or disregard those that do not help define the subject selected from what he saw in the initial scribble lines. The completion of the picture includes using colors according to the wishes of the person drawing.

The scribble stimulates the perception of images appearing in its lines and shapes. However, the choice of the subject associated with the scribble is usually idiosyncratic. The accidental shapes have a good chance of evoking images from the unconscious, thus bringing into the open material that has been repressed. We saw an example of this in Figure 2, "Mother and Child," in Chapter II, which expressed the patient's ambivalence about detaching himself from his mother while he was claiming his desire for independence.

This method was first introduced in artwork with children by Paula Elkisch[12] and Florence Cane.[13]   Margaret Naumburg[2,14] pointed out the scribble as a powerful tool to bring material from the unconscious in her art therapy experiences with adults.

The search for associations while looking at accidental shapes is beautifully described by Leonardo da Vinci in his "Percepts of a Painter" *(Notebooks)*. I feel that what we look for in the inter-crossing lines and resulting forms in the scribble is very close to what he found inspiring and *"arousing the mind"* while looking at old walls:

> A new device for consideration which, although it appears trivial and almost ludicrous, is nevertheless of great utility in *arousing the mind* to various inventions. And that is that if you look at any walls spotted with various stains or with the mixture of different kinds of stones if you are about to invent some scene, you will be able to see

in it a resemblance to various different landscapes adorned with mountains, rivers, rocks, trees, plains, wide valleys and various groups of hills. You will also be able to see diverse faces and outlandish costumes and an infinite number of things which you can then reduce into separate and well conceived forms. . . . With such walls and blends of different stones it comes about as it does with the sound of bells in whose clanging you may discover every name and word that you can imagine.

In my work with families I extended the use of the scribble from an individually developed picture to one in which the whole family participated. First each family member had to make an individual scribble. Then they were all asked to share their associations to what they saw in the lines and shapes of all the scribbles, come to an agreement on an association all saw in one of them and use this theme for a joint picture to be completed together. Each member's personal contribution was expressive of his feelings or his role in the family; this was often noted and commented upon by the rest of the family.

For example, the mother of a twenty-seven-year-old schizophrenic patient painted rather skillful, insipid, conventional pictures of "old fashioned little girls," flowers or landscapes, persistently denying any feelings of anger. She was, however, the one who implanted the set of ferocious teeth in the mouth of the face of a man the family developed together out of a scribble (Fig. 6).

When I called the family's attention to this and the family recognized that the teeth gave the picture an angry, aggressive expression, the mother agreed. She did not deny that it was her contribution that had turned this rather benign head of a young man into someone cruelly devouring. Thus she indirectly acknowledged feelings that she had otherwise carefully concealed. Once she recognized that the constant denial of her real feelings had excluded any meaningful communication with the family, the way was opened for further work in this area in verbal family therapy.

Figure 6.

CHAPTER V

FAMILY ART THERAPY WITH A
HYSTERIC PATIENT AND HER FAMILY

As an example of family art therapy as an adjunctive technique, I am going to describe the course of our work with the Nelson family.* None of the Nelsons had any artistic interest or sophistication. The course of therapy with this family, however, shows that even the most primitive use of graphic symbolism can become a powerful therapeutic tool.

At the time of her admission to the hospital, the patient, Laura, was nineteen. From an early age she had shown signs of emotional imbalance: school phobia from the first grade through the third, paralyzing overdependence on her mother, and a tendency to rituals that verged on psychosis. Before her hospitalization she had had psychotherapy off and on, alone and with her mother. Upon admission her diagnosis was anxiety hysteria with phobic and obsessive-compulsive features.

Laura's mother, Mrs. Nelson, was a slender thirty-nine-year-old woman with a youthful figure, always carefully groomed and dressed with discreet good taste. Through the previous years she had had periods of severe depression that had even led to a serious suicide attempt. She usually came to our sessions very tense and depressed, but she would liven up and become freer while drawing, and, as we shall see, she would discuss her and her family's pictures productively and with considerable animation.

*Excerpts from this case appeared previously in Hanna Yaxa Kwiatkowska. Family art therapy. *Family Process, 6*(1):37-55, 1967.

43

Mr. Nelson, a forty-one-year-old salesman, also had a history of emotional problems; he was a passive-aggressive person with a long history of phobias, somatic complaints, and attacks of severe anxiety. He was more reserved than his wife and slower to recognize and accept the messages in his pictures. However, he gradually become more engaged in the therapeutic process and made use of the family's graphic communications.

Mrs. Nelson's relationship with her husband was very stormy. They argued constantly and even fought physical battles. Mrs. Nelson often threatened to leave the home and once actually did.

Another daughter in the family, fourteen-year-old Dottie, appeared not to be involved in the family conflicts. She made efforts to steer clear, denying that family crises had any impact on her. So far her defenses had worked successfully, and she had her own friends and activities outside the family circle. At the time we saw the Nelsons, her only difficulty was a rather poor scholastic performance, but she was not failing her courses.

It is interesting to note that the parents and also Laura seemed to exclude Dottie from their depictions of family problems. She was usually omitted from pictures representing the most dramatic family situations, while in these pictures Laura was always shown as a sort of pivot around which the parents' relationship revolved.

The parents' problems were so closely related to Laura's that we came to regard the whole family as a "hysteric family." Separation anxiety was one of their major difficulties. Separation precipitated the most dramatic family crises and made the patient's symptoms more severe. Even Laura's return to the hospital after a weekend pass caused trouble.

The family was engaged in an intensive treatment program: conjoint family therapy conducted by a psychiatrist and a social worker, and family art therapy with the same psychiatrist as cotherapist. He also saw Laura individually, while the social worker saw the parents in couple therapy.

The Nelson family responded unexpectedly well to the graphic mode of expression in spite, or perhaps because, of their complete lack of any earlier connection with experience in art. They were unencumbered by the inhibitions of people who admire and understand art and become too concerned with their art product and the standards they set for its aesthetic value.

Art expression of the talented individual may be more appealing and powerful, but the art therapist must convey to the patient that in art therapy, especially in the initial phase, the process takes priority over the product. However, personal growth and insight into basic problems often lead to an impressive improvement of the quality of the art product.

The psychiatrist who participated in both verbal therapy and art therapy with this family was impressed by the difference in their work in the two situations. During the verbal sessions, constant quarrelsome, mordant exchanges between the parents alternated with the patient's monotonous, repetitious description of her symptoms. It was so hard to overcome the word barrier the family set up that the psychiatrist and the social worker conducting these sessions became bored and discouraged.

At the first family art therapy session the parents made the usual protestation about not being artists, about being back in the first grade, etc., before they started drawing. But later in the session the Nelsons recognized with surprise that there was meaning in their pictures and they made full therapeutic use of them. From then on we heard no more complaints about their inability to paint or draw; the family accepted this mode of expression, which seemed to eliminate much of their usual negative verbal communication. They were able to get much more easily to matters of importance without their customary preliminary ritual of bickering or repetitious complaints.

In the course of the forty-five family art therapy sessions, the parents and Laura attended regularly, with only an occasional absence by one or the other of the parents. Dottie, however, appeared at only a few of the sessions; she and her parents made excuses related to her school schedule. Dottie had some learning difficulties and felt that missing classes would make it still harder for her to keep up with her studies. We accepted these excuses, seeing Dottie's absence as her effort to avoid involvement in family problems. Our supposition was later confirmed by the pictures she drew when she did take part in family art therapy.

The art therapy sessions were not structured; the family was encouraged to draw whatever came to mind. Hard pastels and tempera paints were available, and a couple of stimulative art therapy techniques, such as the individual and family scribbles, were gradually introduced. The quality of the family's art productions was rather primitive, but each family member had his or her distinctive style. There was some similarity between Laura's and her mother's pictures.

Most of Mrs. Nelson's early pictures were schematic representations of situations enacted by rudimentarily drawn figures (Fig. 7). As the art therapy sessions were coming to a close, we were surprised to see a change to a freer and aesthetically more pleasing style (Fig. 8).

Figure 7.

Despite his lack of much contact with or interest in art, Mr. Nelson's pictures, initially quite naive and drawn without regard to perspective and correct proportions, gradually revealed an unexpected skill. Their artistic quality improved on the occasions when he was able to break away from his usual sullen remoteness and let himself express his feelings without self-imposed restraint.

Both Laura and Dottie were not particularly preoccupied with the quality of their artwork. Dottie produced few pictures in her sporadic attendance in the art sessions and we did not see much

Figure 8.

change in them. Laura's initial pictures, which were either rigidly controlled ("Confusion," Fig. 9) or cryptically schematic (Fig. 10), somewhat like her mother's (Fig. 7), gradually gained some freedom and quality. They always conveyed a message, however.

Judging from the Nelsons' attitude in verbal family therapy, we expected to meet with more difficulties in the family art sessions than turned out to be the case. It soon became clear to us that the art therapy technique was suitable for this family.

Dottie was not present at the first session. The parents and Laura were just asked to make a picture of whatever came to mind. As frequently occurs, Laura's first picture, "Confusion" (Fig. 9), was a graphic self-introduction. She explained, "It is just a bunch of things that don't make any sense . . . but they're all inside of something very rigid." This was an eloquent representation of her inner confusion contained in a shell of rigid, obsessive-compulsive defenses.

In using art with families, I found that houses often appear as

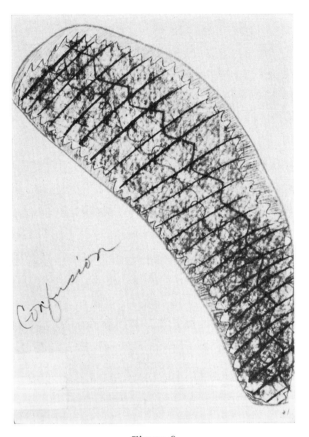

Figure 9.

the subject of first pictures by one or both of the parents as things supposedly easy to draw. Most of the time, however, they carry memories, wishes and associations to the past or the present. Mr. and Mrs. Nelson's pictures are good examples.

Mrs. Nelson's first picture, a naive representation of a house (Fig. 11), made her wonder why she had drawn a two-story house when the family was living in a rambler: "That's just what came to my mind. . . . I don't know why I made it two stories. . . . I lived in one as a child and there was a lot of happiness at that time."

Figure 10.

Mr. Nelson's first pictures were on a more conscious level; he presented himself indirectly as a person with unfulfilled wishes in life and with interests not shared by his family. His very first picture was of the boat he had never owned but always wished for (not shown). His second picture was a "Country Club" (Fig. 12), with the putting green on the left. He said regretfully that he never went there because no one in his family was interested in going.

After their first try at freely drawn pictures, the family was introduced to the scribble technique. Laura was reluctant to use it; she had planned at this session to draw "a rose," apparently to escape from an expression of more genuine feelings. What she finally decided to elaborate from the lines of her scribble seemed fairly innocuous: a bowling pin (Fig. 13). But Laura's comments gave it a more personal meaning: The bowling pin was to be used "to hit somebody." Then she observed that "it was nailed so that it couldn't move" (see nail at lower part of the pin). She

Figure 11.

Figure 12.

wistfully added, "I wish it could have been a rose."

This statement seemed to express a wish to deny the real feelings she had expressed metaphorically with such clarity in her scribble picture: her ambivalence and her hostile dependency on her mother.

Mrs. Nelson commented upon her own picture (Fig. 14), started with the help of a scribble:

> The first thing I thought of was a yo-yo and the string is all tangled . . . and that's a tear drop at the side . . . like my childhood. . . . Of course, a yo-yo is a childs' toy. . . . I don't know if I am crying because the string is all twisted and I cannot unravel it or I am crying because I am no longer a child.

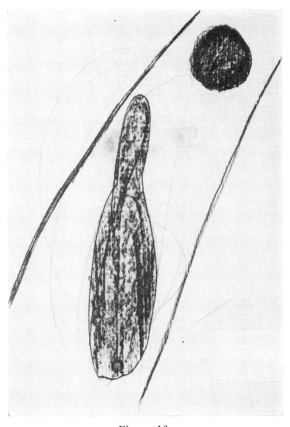

Figure 13.

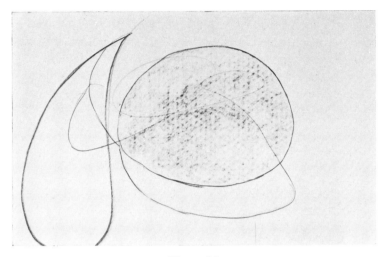

Figure 14.

In the case of both mother and daughter we can see that the picture started by a scribble is more genuine and less controlled by the superego than is the free picture. Mrs. Nelson had at first mentioned "a lot of happiness" in her childhood home, but later, in the drawing initiated by her scribble, she saw a huge "tear drop . . . like my childhood" thus contradicting the happiness of her childhood depicted in her first drawing.

Mr. Nelson's first scribble picture, "Christmas Tree Ball" (not shown), did not bring out associations as personal and significant as those of his wife's and daughter's. However, he admitted to having other thoughts about it that he preferred to keep to himself. We can surmise that because Laura and her mother had had therapy previously, they were freer to talk about their feelings than he was. But in a picture of a childhood memory that he made later (Fig. 15), Mr. Nelson eventually brought up deeper, more personal and painful experiences, although he did not connect them openly with his present life situation.

The picture represented a house with a tennis court on which, he said, he had never played. It was his parental home, where he had had a most miserable childhood. His parents had separated when he was five years old, after which he and his sisters lived

Figure 15.

with their mother and stepfather. He never had his own room; he slept in the attic until he was twenty, but his sisters had every comfort. He presented himself as having been abused and rejected by the women of his childhood, just as he felt treated by his wife and daughters.

Mrs. Nelson, out of touch with her husband's affective experience, heard only his regret about the tennis court, seeing it as similar to his desire to own a boat or play golf at the country club. She disregarded completely the pain and sense of rejection he was finally able to express and commented coldly, "All Jack's pictures tell me that he is looking for pleasure."

The Nelson family responded well to the scribble technique and particularly to the joint scribble, of which they made frequent use on their own initiative. This proved to be a way they could tell what they thought and how they felt toward each other without causing too much hurt or provoking violent arguments. They noticed their differing ways of looking at themselves and their differing ways of dealing with their problems. The family repeatedly saw self-images in these jointly developed pictures.

At the third session a scribble picture was developed jointly by the family into a clown (Plate III). The family quickly agreed to father's association to the lines of the scribble, and initially they all participated in an amused fashion. But at one point Mr. Nelson became concerned because the clown did not have a happy expression; he tried unsuccessfully to force a smile at the corners of the clown's mouth. Finally he gave up and said sadly, "If I looked like that I wouldn't want to smile either," thus identifying with the image of the clown. Further, he entitled the picture "Sorry Clown." This picture can be seen as an indirect self-presentation, his view of himself and of his pitiful role in the family. We can see here a continuation of his messages in his first pictures of the boat he never had and the country club he never went to (Fig. 12); later the same feeling is conveyed in the picture of his childhood home (Fig. 15).

Both mother and daughter were uneasy about the clown's sadness; they did not want to accept the title "Sorry Clown" and insisted that Mr. Nelson cross out the "Sorry." Here we see again how hard it was for this mother and daughter to see him as different from the image of him generally accepted by the family. At this point they were not ready to recognize his feeling of being rejected and his sadness.

It will be interesting to compare the "Sorry Clown" with a picture of similar subject drawn by this father alone at a much later date, toward the end of the treatment (thirty-second session).

"Clown or Comedian" (Plate IV) was drawn without the help of a scribble, and although Mr. Nelson at first denied that it was a self-portrait, he gradually recognized that it was. The dimples he drew on this face seemed to be his trademark; he had, in fact, pronounced dimples when he smiled. We can conclude that at that point he still saw himself as the "comedian" who hid his real feelings, but at the same time the expression of this clown is self-assured and happier, and he can allow himself to smile.

At the session following the "Sorry Clown" (Plate III), we obtained a view of how Mrs. Nelson perceived her role in the family.

"The Ogre" (Fig. 16) was jointly created by Mr. and Mrs.

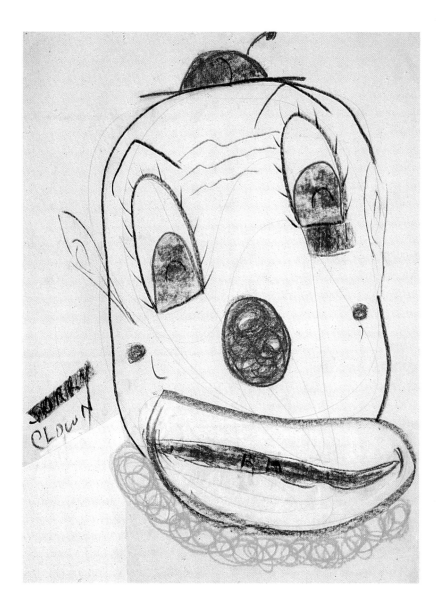

Plate III.

Plate IV.

Nelson and Laura from a scribble; Dottie was not present. It was Mrs. Nelson's suggestion that they make a joint picture started by a scribble, but she urged Laura to make the initial lines. Mrs. Nelson saw in the scribble "a horn of plenty," and Laura saw "a mother and baby." Mrs. Nelson then drew an outline in brown, which she called a "fetus." Mr. Nelson called this shape "a cat." But Laura said, "It is a piece of fried shrimp." Finally Mr. Nelson took the lead, urging Laura to outline a face. After she did so, he worked on the features, trying to "make the face smile." "She's got a mask on her face," he commented.

Figure 16.

The atmosphere was at first relaxed and playful but soon became exceedingly tense. Mr. Nelson said, "Might as well try to make the face sad. I was trying to dress up this face a bit, to make it nice and matronly." Mrs. Nelson, who had been silent and did not take much part in the drawing, was then asked by the psychiatrist-cotherapist what she saw in the face. "It is an ogre," she said. "I have been accused many times by my husband of being an ogre. It was I who had to do all the disciplining of the children, which he never did; I knew that this had to backfire on me." The husband and wife began to argue with each other. Laura became increasingly anxious and tried to take the blame for the change in the picture. She said regretfully, "I was the one who started the face, I wanted it to be pretty. . . . That face looks mean, not only glaring but mean!" She was caught in her parents' conflict and distressed by her own ambivalent feelings toward her mother.

With the help of images that emerged unplanned and to which the family responded genuinely, the family members gradually began to understand other aspects of their view of themselves and of each other and were able to work on their relationships in both the art and the verbal family sessions.

We also became more aware of Dottie's efforts to avoid any involvement in family problems. The following pictures give us striking examples of the role of the "well" sibling in disturbed families.[16]

Because of her school schedule, Dottie did not join the family group until the sixth meeting. In the sessions her attitude was mostly one of denial. The difference between the "well" sibling who manages to remain somehow uninvolved in the family's problems and the patient who is sucked into them was particularly noticeable in the two sisters' pictures at the ninth session. Mr. Nelson was absent for reasons presumably related to work, but Mrs. Nelson spoke of a violent argument that she had had with him during the weekend. Laura first tried to use gay colors in tricky drippings of paint. Then, during a discussion of the father's absence, she suddenly said, "Well, I'd better not pretend . . .," and smeared the whole sheet with heavy black strokes (Fig.

17) ; she titled this picture "Black Mood." In contrast, Dottie painted at the same session a "Happy Mood" (Plate V) in light, gay, dancing strokes, with a predominance of orange, pink and yellow and some touches of light blue. Through this picture she denied having any feelings about her father's absence or about her parents' argument, in contrast to Laura's depression and anger expressed in her "Black Mood" picture.

Figure 17.

At the same session Mrs. Nelson drew a picture that climaxed the events of the weekend, "A Man Throwing a Woman Out of the House" (Fig. 18). She remarked, when she first looked at her drawing, that one of the people looked like a "pregnant girl with a baby." She then labeled the two figures with her own and her husband's names. The patient said, "*I* might be the pregnant girl chased away from the house by my father," suggesting that some oedipal fantasies had been aroused in her by this picture.

In art therapy the Nelsons were constantly bringing up problems vital to each family member and to the whole family.

Figure 18.

Images have the peculiar power to bring speedily to the surface deep material that is escaping strict superego control. After a time this may effect an increase of resistance often manifested by a demeaning attitude toward art therapy, denial that the pictures mean anything, and a revival of all the initial protestations about lack of talent or interest. This occurred with the Nelsons.

In the third month of treatment, after their pictures were bringing out more and more material that touched upon genuine feelings and crucial problems, the Nelson family started to express doubts about the usefulness of art therapy sessions. The therapists then suggested a review of the family's work to help them understand what was actually happening.

As mentioned earlier, the permanence of the art products provides an opportunity unavailable by any other means. Looking at the pictures created earlier often revives the emotional impact of the experience at the time they were drawn, yet there is distance between creating the pictures and reviewing them later. The catharsis achieved by expressing intense feelings graphically allows the individual to face more easily later what may have

Plate V.

Plate VI.

been difficult to acknowledge at the start; the review of the pictures carries the message but is free of some of the intensity of those feelings.

At the preceding session Laura had drawn scribbled loops of different colors (Plate VI) and was quite shaken when, after finishing it, she said, "I really felt like I was writing all over 'I hate you, I hate you, I hate you.' " But while reviewing the pictures she looked at it calmly and accepted my comment, "Would it have been possible to express hateful feelings without this picture?" This led Laura to notice in turn the repetitive symmetrical lines in another of her pictures as a true representation of her increased compulsion at the time she drew it.

The psychiatrist-cotherapist was quite direct in his interpretation of Mr. Nelson's fears of touching upon difficult or controversial subjects in his pictures. For example, a rigid picture of a vase with flowers drawn during the preceding session was an obvious effort to do something as meaningless as possible (not shown).

Gradually the family became engrossed in viewing and commenting on their past pictures, and this led eventually to their working on a joint scribble picture (not shown). While they were doing it, they were alert to the way they went about it. Mrs. Nelson commented that she did not take any initiative because she was called the domineering and aggressive one. The therapists pointed out how hard it was for the family to make a joint decision and cited this as an important justification for continuing the art sessions. After that there was no more talk for a long while of the uselessness of art therapy. Nevertheless, we felt that many of the family's reactions to the pictures were not sufficiently explored; the Nelsons seemed afraid to commit themselves.

We were still faced from time to time by resistance on the part of the Nelson family. After a more intense session either someone would miss the next session or there would be an overproduction of insignificant pictures. Such overproduction, observed in a number of families, becomes a resistance maneuver, an escape from the exploration of the projected material. At other times the Nelsons would be totally apathetic and uncommunicative. The therapists felt that a more active approach would be beneficial and we soon had an opportunity to try it.

In their twentieth session the parents and Laura were extremely depressed and listless; Dottie was absent on that day. They all sat in silence until finally the mother got up and drew in pastel a brown layer of what she called "muck and quagmire" (Fig. 19). She said it was something like quicksand, in which she and her husband were sinking. Maybe they were already under and there was nobody to pull them out. I wondered aloud how anybody who was nearby would know that they were sinking if there was no hand reaching out for help. The mother then drew a hand sticking out of the mud, and the group returned to its depressed silence.

Figure 19.

At this moment the cotherapist went into action. He drew a helicopter above the hand reaching for help and inscribed on it "NIH" (National Institutes of Health), with a rope ladder hanging from it.

The family quickly came to life. Mr. Nelson drew two little figures which, he explained, were Laura in the helicopter and himself on the rope ladder; Mrs. Nelson was left out. Laura in turn drew in stronger black a little figure representing her father in the helicopter. She then drew an incomplete one-legged figure representing herself stretched between her father in the helicopter and her mother's hand sticking out of the mud. Her outstretched foot touched the hand of the drowning mother. Laura explained that this represented both giving her mother help and seeking help from her. This prompted Mrs. Nelson to speak tearfully about her relationship with her own mother and her resentment and grief at never having been close to her.

No interpretation was made of another possible meaning of Laura's contribution to the picture; it might have represented an oedipal fantasy of taking off in the helicopter with her father, leaving her mother stuck in the mud.

The picture is dramatic despite its simplicity. The genuine feelings projected through this drawing, particularly the despair and the unformulated plea for help the mother expressed in such a primitive manner, contrasted strongly with the quarreling and lack of real feeling that remained characteristic of the Nelsons' verbal therapy sessions.

This session was a turning point in therapy. The family began to feel that help was available, that they could trust the therapists to help them out of the "quagmire" of their problems. It should be noted that Dottie was not included in this turning-point picture, nor was she included in other pictures that were markedly significant in touching on family conflict.

In the course of treatment, both underlying and immediate problems of the family kept appearing in the pictures, opening the way to further exploration in the verbal sessions, in which the Nelsons became livelier and more productive than in the initial period. Gradually, improvement in the family relations was noted. Although crises in the family life occasionally occurred, the family members were willing to deal with them in both art and verbal therapy and did not insist on ignoring the communications carried in their pictures.

At the time treatment was terminated, Laura's symptoms had abated to such an extent that she could lead a less dependent life. For a time she stayed in the hospital but worked in the community. Then she was discharged and she returned to college. While still in the hospital she started dating a young man whom she eventually married. They had a child to whom she devoted most of her time.

Mr. and Mrs. Nelson were better able to accept and understand each other. No longer were they blinded by the mutual hostility that often had been misdirected at Laura. They continued to have frequent quarrels, but as far as we know there were no more threats of suicide. However, a much later follow-up revealed that they eventually were divorced. Dottie improved her scholastic performance, entered college and attained a degree. She managed to keep herself out of the conflict and maintain her role of the "well" sibling.

CHAPTER VI

FAMILIES OF SCHIZOPHRENICS
AS SEEN THROUGH
THEIR ART PRODUCTIONS

During the early years of our use of art with families as an adjunct to family therapy, we made a number of interesting and intriguing discoveries. Family dynamics were clearly displayed, and specific patterns of perception and behavior were found to be characteristic in families of different diagnostic groups.

Most of the ward population in those early years consisted of young adult schizophrenic patients, and initial incidental participation of family members in the art sessions became more and more illustrative of the peculiar aspects of the experience with schizophrenic families. The display of the interactional and perceptual patterns of different family members and of subgroups within the family provided rich material to be explored in therapy and for research.

We noticed that the art productions of different members of the family often showed more striking similarities in styles of thinking and perceiving than was evident in other transactions with them. Most of these parents and siblings had not developed overt psychiatric symptoms and were functioning fairly effectively in their jobs or their studies. Upon scrutiny, however, we found that in most of the families we investigated, other family members were also affected to varying degrees by a severe underlying disturbance of perception or thought. This schizophrenic tendency was more blatant in the family member recognized as the patient; it was masked in the parents and siblings. Through the pictures and the families' comments on them we were able to identify some of the patterns of thinking common to the parents and to the patients and their siblings:

1. An amorphous, blurred perception of reality: Thoughts drift off without the object of attention and perception ever becoming clearly delineated or formulated.

2. Fragmented thinking: Disruption and disorganization of thinking after attention has been initially focused and perceptions formed.

3. An overorganized, obsessional, paranoid way of thinking: The thinking is so excessively coherent, rigid and constricted that it leaves out essential feelings such as love, anger, etc.

Family art therapy with the Williams family, who were discussed in Chapters I and IV, provided many examples of behavioral and perceptional material that we later found to be characteristic of schizophrenic families. In both mother's and daughter's behavior and pictures we can notice the easily interrupted continuity of thought in schizophrenic processes. A dramatic scene of anger and reproach can change abruptly into a meaningless exchange when attention shifts to an accidental detail in the environment. For example, to a flow of Peggy's screams, insults and reproaches about being abandoned and unloved, and even to bodily attacks, Mrs. Williams would respond with equally mordant and hostile outbursts. Then, at the most dramatic moment, Peggy would suddenly shift to an entirely different tone and with great interest describe to her mother "a darling little dress" she had seen in a fashion magazine. They would both then talk vivaciously about clothes and parties, completely cut off from their immediately preceding painful experience, while I was still shaken by the violent hatred and aggression they had displayed only minutes earlier.

Their pictures provided an excellent illustration of the disruption of goal-oriented, purposeful thought. The final pictorial representation can become irrelevant to the initial aim. We see this in a picture Peggy drew from nature (Plate VII). She worked hard to reproduce what she saw, repeatedly saying, "I like things to look real." But upon scrutiny we can see that the blue sky is suddenly interrupted by the trunk of the tree, which seems to cut it off. Similarly, the outline of the hill breaks off when it reaches the branch and leaves. The background is broken into three separate segments.

This picture strikes us as a graphic representation of the same phenomenon in verbal communication. The sound of a word brings forth an association that has no logical relation to the word's meaning (clang association). Either a new sound or a new shape presents a barrier that cuts off the initial message and causes a shift to a new, incidental idea irrelevant to the initial one.

We see something similar in Mrs. Williams picture (Plate VIII) representing a landscape. We cannot quite believe that the two brown "roads," as she called them, shooting into the air are only the result of faulty perspective. The roads cross each other and stop abruptly in the sky, while the touch of blue on the middle right cuts off the continuation of the shape of the hill, much like what appears in Peggy's picture (Plate VII). Similar distortions appear in numerous other pictures by both mother and daughter.

THE USE OF THE SCRIBBLE IN DIAGNOSIS

The use of the scribble presents important clues in the diagnosis of schizophrenic subjects and their families. How well an individual can integrate the lines and shapes of a scribble into a picture is often indicative of how his thinking is organized. Figure 20, "A Girl," is an example of a creative and beautifully integrated use of scribble lines by a woman in her thirties who was both talented and emotionally stable.

The schizophrenic in an acute psychotic state is usually unable to cope with this task. He will see shapes obtained by the lines of the scribble only as separate fragments and will not succeed in organizing them into a unified whole (Fig. 21). Process schizo-

Figure 20.

phrenics of the undifferentiated type would often completely disregard the scribble and make a drawing over it or next to it; see, for example, Figure 22, "A Mess."

Plate VII.

Plate VIII.

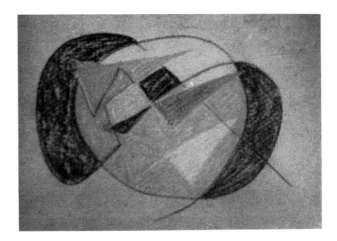

Figure 21.

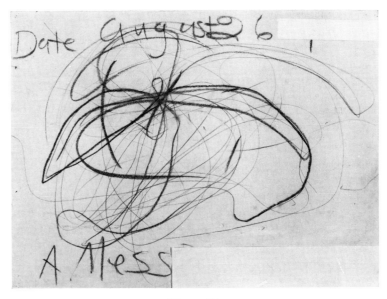

Figure 22.

Occasionally we observed that patients would choose a small portion of the scribble, frequently at the edge of the whole scribble shape, and outline it (Fig. 23). This is most frequently

Figure 23.

seen in borderline patients with occasional schizophrenic breaks.

The schizophrenic with obsessive-compulsive traits will draw and redraw the initial lines of the scribble, reinforcing the outlines and carefully filling in with colors each resulting area (Fig. 24). In her individual sessions Peggy Williams drew innumerable scribble pictures, all with similar characteristics even though they were drawn at different periods in her treatment, as we see in Figures 25 and 26. Figure 24, however, is more rigid than the two later examples. Sexual symbolism is evident in the powerful phallic shape on the left. Peggy did not comment directly on it, but throughout the preceding couple of sessions she had spoken of her feelings of "badness" in connection with past sexual experiences. Her rigid religious beliefs resulted in guilt feelings and fear of punishment. The sexual symbol may also have aroused her defenses and could account for the greater rigidity of this particular scribble picture.

Figure 25, "Abstraction," was done a year later, and Figure

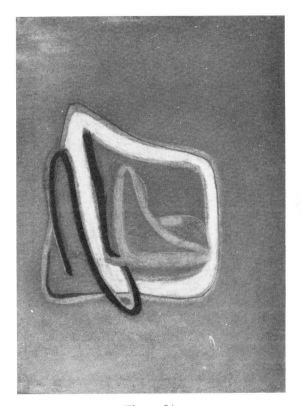

Figure 24.

26, untitled, three months after that. They are a little less constricted, but we observe the same retracing of the original lines of the scribble that are not integrated into a composition. The shapes are left open and unconnected; lines suddenly stop short, mostly with one shooting out into space.

We can see something much the same in her mother's picture (Plate VIII), in which the two roads end in midair and have a similar sharply incomplete or cutoff quality.

These similarities between Peggy's and her mother's pictures led to speculation on the connection between the forms of thinking and perceiving of parents and the ensuing psychopathological disorders in their offspring. Work with the Williams family, one

Figure 25.

of the first with which we used art techniques, opened our eyes to how much this joint activity reveals the family's perceptual and interactional styles.

The joint scribble picture, "Flying Duck" (Fig. 27), by Peggy

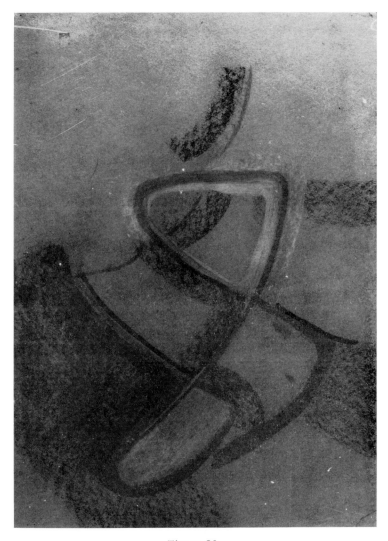

Figure 26.

and her parents, not only bears the impact of Peggy's style, but also demonstrates the inability of both parents to deal with her distortions of meaning and perception; it was started from the father's free-flowing scribble. Peggy's first association was that of "a flying duck." Neither of the parents saw it, but they went along with Peggy's idea. Later the father tried to protest the peculiar position of the duck's feet. Peggy insisted that "the feet just have to be that way!" The father grew more and more annoyed; he tried to join Peggy in drawing, adding a blue pond and a marsh on the left. The mother added "snow flowers" on the left and blue lines in the sky. Peggy became angry and monopolized the picture, elaborating the meaningless blue multiangular shape, a part of Mr. Williams' initial scribble. The mother suggested the title "Ugly Duckling."

Figure 27.

We notice here that Peggy imposed her style, of which we saw examples in her individual scribbles (Figs. 24, 25, 26), reinforcing and retracing the initial lines of the scribble without regard to the subject agreed upon. We further see that her parents passively accepted irrationality, distortion of meaning, and misrepresentation. They accepted their daughter's initial idea for the picture, her skewing of the duck's feet, and her accentuation of the accidental linear pattern. This last detracted substantially from their initial choice of subject. The parents neither defined reality for Peggy nor expected realistic thought or behavior of her.

In Figure 28, a joint scribble done two months later, Mr. Williams took the lead, carried through his own interpretation of the scribble, and did most of the drawing. On this day Mrs. Williams and Peggy were apathetic and withdrawn; their contribution was minimal. In the scribble the father immediately saw a farmhouse on a hill with a big road (later changed to a ravine) leading to it and began to draw this scene. His wife contributed the sheep on the upper right and the bull on the lower right, complaining all the while about her inability to draw and asking me for a lot of help. Peggy followed her father's work with some interest but did not impose her own ideas or additions; she remained more the spectator.

Figure 28.

In this instance the father was not swayed by his wife's and daughter's views; he was able to portray reality without gross distortion. In contrast, in the earlier situation (Fig. 27), the daughter had expressed her opinion more actively and forcefully; the father's highly organized, narrowly focused, obsessional way of functioning did not allow him to utilize his experience or his commonsense observation to combat her distortion.

This inability to deal with unreality or distortion of reality when both parents behave in this fashion was observed in the joint artwork of other families of schizophrenic persons and may be predictive of schizophrenic thought disorder in one of the offspring.

DENIAL OF MEANING

Other aspects of our work with the Williams family also proved to be typical of what we later observed repeatedly in other families of schizophrenics.

Mrs. Williams drew "Sunning" (Fig. 29) during one of her individual art therapy sessions. She talked about it while she drew; it clearly expressed her desire to escape from the problem of Peggy's illness. She commented on the gay pink house on the beach, with a smiling sun and a person sunning herself: "Here I am, in Spain, lying in the sun, away from everything." As if feeling guilty about this escape fantasy, she added, "Of course, if things get settled down with Peggy." It is noteworthy that when her daughter barged in, as she often did during her mother's individual sessions, Mrs. Williams transferred to Peggy what she had earlier said about herself: "This is you, Peggy, lying in the sun." But when Peggy left the room, she continued to talk in the first person about the figure on the beach, thus merging Peggy and herself into one person.

This picture, together with Mrs. Williams' comments, illustrates something we came upon often in our work with the families of schizophrenic patients. The picture stimulated Mrs. Williams to express freely an escape fantasy, and this evoked feelings of guilt. The meaning of the picture was therefore quickly altered in the presence of her daughter. She also shifted back and

Figure 29.

forth the identity of the person sunning herself, suggesting her symbiotic relationship with her daughter.

Finally, when it was mentioned at the later individual session that the picture expressed some of her feelings, she quickly denied everything: "It doesn't mean anything; today I wouldn't go away for anything in the world."

She was unable to acknowledge a feeling she had perceived momentarily when it was projected in her picture and could not sustain continuity of such feeling. Her desire to escape from her struggle with Peggy's illness was well justified and was probably pervasive and constant. But by later denying the meaning of her drawing, she reduced her drawing to a momentary response to an immediate stimulus. Such denial of meaning is one of the most characteristic features we found in families of schizophrenics.

An especially striking example of how it is to get family members of schizophrenics to acknowledge meaning occurred in connection with the picture "My Dream" (Fig. 30) drawn by Mrs. Harmon, the fifty-year-old mother of John, her twenty-five-year-old schizophrenic son. This mother, although functioning quite effectively as a professional woman, was obsessed with constipation. She felt dirty and filled with disgusting fecal matter, and engaged in long, costly medical treatment. She was quite involved in the art therapy sessions and drew interesting pictures, but it was difficult to get her to perceive and accept the message they carried.

Figure 30.

Figure 30 represents a situation astonishingly similar to that in the helicopter picture of the Nelson family (Fig. 19). In it too we see a hand emerging from mud and dirty water. The mother commented,

> This is the middle of this lake, but it is thick, ugly, maybe human excrement. . . . The hand stretched out is artificial, a sort of buoy. . . . I didn't mean to make this human, like a drowning person; it's tin, a sign, wooden. This looks like me on the left. . . . I just had this vision of my torso being held. . . . It was all seen through the water.

She addressed her husband:

> You grabbed me when I shrieked "help." . . . I was drowning

in a nightmare and he was in bed and actually grabbed me when I was still asleep. I don't know what would have happened if I had the dream and if he weren't there, whether I would have drowned or awakened myself.

One feels here a confusion between dream and reality. The dream was depicted and described by her in literal fashion; its elements are specific but lifeless. She insisted that the hand was made of tin or wood and failed to associate it with a human hand possibly reaching out for help.

None of the three other family members participating in the session responded to the picture; no one saw a possible message in it. I felt completely isolated, and my attempts to make use of the picture came to nothing. Nothing happened, nobody was moved. A drama was painted but there was no drama; the dream might as well not have been painted.*

THERAPISTS' SUBJECTIVE EXPERIENCE WITH FAMILIES OF SCHIZOPHRENIC PATIENTS

A comparison of the Nelsons' session, discussed in Chapter V, with that of the Harmons, discussed above, will highlight some features peculiar to working with schizophrenic families.

In the Nelson family, the identified patient was hysteric; in the Harmon family, schizophrenic. While the message in Mrs. Nelson's picture ("Helicopter," Fig. 19) was fruitfully therapeutically explored, all efforts to make comparable use of the strikingly similar message in Mrs. Harmon's picture ("My Dream," Fig. 30) failed.

Schaffer et al.[17] aptly summarized the therapist's peculiar experience with families of schizophrenics:

> The quality of the experience with families of schizophrenics seems strangely different from that in work with other families, although the latter may be hardly less arduous at times. One is likely to emerge from a session at least somewhat less confident of the integrity of one's senses, to say nothing of the value of previously — and sometimes subsequently — held beliefs and conceptions concerning psychiatry.

---

*From Hanna Yaxa Kwiatkowska. Family art therapy. *Family Process*, 6(1):37-55, 1967.

These feelings are acutely experienced in sessions in which art is used as the main form of communication. Frequently pictures appear to be loaded with rich symbolism and verbal comments are abundant. Yet the therapists feel that something is escaping their grasp; it is hard for them to follow and remember the family's interpretations of their pictures. Later, after having carefully studied the tape recordings of such sessions, we found that what had seemed so significant was devoid of meaning, remote from any genuine experience.

The family art therapy session reproduces to a degree the habitual transactions of the family's everyday life. Therefore the therapist is confronted with the lifelong responses and relationships of parents and their offspring. After a while he is swept into the family pattern and, to an extent, experiences what it must have been like for a child exposed to this atmosphere from birth.

An hour-and-twenty-minute art evaluation session with Mrs. Carreri and her unmarried thirty-seven-year-old daughter Rita provides an enlightening example of the therapist's experience with these families.

This mother-daughter session took place during a later period of my work with families, when the more structured procedures of family art evaluation had been designed; they were used in this case.

Mrs. Carreri, a widow, was in her late sixties. She was a stout lady, bespectacled, unpretentiously dressed. Her ankles were swollen, her hearing impaired. During the session she complained abundantly about her ailments.

She had borne three children, all of whom became schizophrenic to varying degrees. Rita, the daughter participating in the art evaluation session, was diagnosed as schizophrenic, chronic undifferentiated type. She had had several previous hospitalizations because of severe psychotic and psychosomatic symptoms, hallucinations, rituals, rocking and vomiting. She had undergone treatment including electroshock and, later, drug therapy (Trilafon® and chlorpromazine). Between these psychotic episodes, she was able to function adequately, though on a somewhat marginal level, and even to work.

At the time of her admission to the Clinical Center of the National Institutes of Health, Rita was quite disorganized, engaging in paralyzing, obsessive rituals and complaints, rocking and vomiting. In individual psychotherapy she avoided bringing issues into the open. She was fuzzy and compulsively stewed over the same complaints again and again.

The family art evaluation session, in which only the mother and Rita took part, was minimally productive and seemed to drag on interminably. It was hard to believe that so much time had been used to produce their meager images. It illustrated vividly both the relationship between mother and daughter and the paucity of their inner world.

Mrs. Carreri used her helplessness to make such forceful demands that they were hard to resist. I was so busy jumping around Mrs. Carreri that at times I barely noticed Rita. I felt as if Rita and I were teamed up to help and protect Mrs. Carreri. At the same time Mrs. Carreri engendered an overwhelming feeling of guilt. It seemed to me at times that I was virtually murdering this lady, abusing her and exploiting her. Maybe this was in part a response to Mrs. Carreri's insistently repeated questions about what would be done with this session. Would the pictures be reproduced? Would the session serve as material for a book? Her last question was to a degree justified, because the unusual case of her schizophrenic offspring had been described in psychiatric literature. I found myself apologizing and reassuring her, but at the same time angry with her because I could not resist her demands.

Throughout the session Rita constantly sought physical contact with her mother, whining over and over, "Oh Mama, dear Mama!" She kept touching her mother, patting her on her shoulder, to which Mrs. Carreri responded by barking angrily, "Don't pat me!" To her mother's constant complaints about her inability, her worthlessness in this situation, Rita responded by saying encouragingly, "That's all right, Mama." One wonders whether it was especially difficult for this pocket-battleship of a mother to tolerate a situation in which she felt so inadequate in the presence of her daughter. The daughter, in contrast to her mother, responded to the task unexpectedly well, considering her emotional state at the time. Throughout the session, however, Rita continued to whine, "Oh Mama, dear Mama," twisting her hair and clinging to Mrs. Carreri, at the same time both protecting her mother and seeking protection from her.

All of Mrs. Carreri's pictures were most crude and primitive. But as the session progressed, her complaints and self-depreciation diminished, and occasionally she recognized some connection between her meager images and their possible meaning. For example, a practically unrecognizable cane derived from a scribble evoked the comment, "I guess that's what I am going to walk on."

Her picture "Clouds" (Fig. 31) reduced her to tears. The clouds are drawn with just a few light blue, barely visible lines, one large cloud (herself?) with four smaller ones above it (her children and husband?). She remarked, "I feel that I have . . . I am in clouds." Rita echoed, "Yes, Mama." Mrs. Carreri continued, "They was [sic] big and big, and then they got a little bit

Figure 31.

smaller . . . and then they were large again." She burst into tears, with Rita meanwhile whining, "Mama, dear Mama."

Mrs. Carreri's emotional outburst led us to believe that she had reacted to the possible symbolism of her picture. The clouds "got a little bit smaller" during a period of relative adjustment of her children, who somehow functioned, although at different levels. Then, when Rita had to be again hospitalized, "they were large again." This mood lasted only a short while. Mrs. Carreri quickly pulled herself together, looked at the clock, and said something about her next appointment.

In the aridity of the whole experience, these tiny rays of genuine feeling help the therapist survive. They are so gratifying that they evoke an intense feeling of warmth and closeness—a gift that makes up for the earlier confusion, guilt and resentment.

This kind of personal experience helps the therapist understand the strength of the ties between the schizophrenic offspring and his parent.

In this particular case, I was faced with an ambiguous situation. As a researcher, I was attuned to observing and noting manifestations of psychopathology. As a therapist, I was responding strongly to a hopeful moment when I sensed that Mrs. Carreri was sharing with me a feeling, even if so indirectly. I was so grateful for her gift of a few seconds of closeness that I was ready to repeat after Rita, "Oh Mama, dear Mama."

The effort to reach the family in their blurred or fragmented experience may appear to be an impossible task; it is, however, a challenging one. Art therapy has a particular advantage. Despite all the vagueness of the family's verbal interpretation of their artwork, that work remains in evidence. Unlike words, it is not evanescent. Therefore it may become a stepping stone toward communication with the family across the curtain of their distortion and denial of meaning. Although work with schizophrenic patients and their families is an unusually taxing and draining experience, the use of art media presents some unique values, which help in the arduous communication with these families.

The permanence and tangibility of the art products has proved to be an irreplaceable means of focusing the family's attention on a subject and keeping it there. Further, these same qualities make it possible to return to a subject until it is sufficiently explored. A single picture has at times been used in several successive sessions; we could return to it at the meeting following its production and achieve a degree of continuity often impossible in verbal therapy. Through the picture, reality often confronted denial. Presented in the picture, the distortion of one family member's perception of another could be clarified, advancing the therapeutic process.

CHAPTER VII

FAMILY ART EVALUATION

THE CLINICAL examples described in preceding chapters led to the gradual emergence and development of structured evaluative art procedures with families. This chapter will deal with the exploration of the total series of tasks that came to be called family art evaluation.

This method was at first introduced and used with the majority of investigated families at the National Institute of Mental Health. Later, family art evaluation became a routine procedure in numerous institutions, mental health centers, etc., because of the strikingly rich and accurate view of the family relations and dynamics that could be obtained with great economy of family and staff time.

This broadening of the application and expansion of family evaluative procedures has undergone modifications and changes of its initial design by clinicians and researchers according to their orientation and focus of their interests. However, many years of experimentation and study of the use of families' art productions for diagnostic and research purposes made me believe that the most reliable and unbiased material is obtained through the method described below.

The family art evaluation consists of a single meeting (sometimes extended, as discussed in Chapter II, to a second session) of all nuclear family members who are available. Younger children and others who for one reason or another do not participate in verbal conjoint family therapy are also invited. Their presence often sheds additional light on the family's style, roles and relationships. The younger child has proved at times to be most valuable in revealing the family dynamics or family secrets.

While the family art therapy sessions were unstructured, we noticed that certain subjects appeared spontaneously in the work of a number of families. These subjects stimulated a great deal of discussion by family members or were exceptionally illuminating of family dynamics. We therefore organized these subjects into a series of procedures applied in a particular sequence.

We have found it best for the art therapist to know in advance only the family's socioeconomic and educational status and their respective ages. Thus the diagnostic clues and conclusions are drawn only from the pictures and the family interaction during the evaluation session. It is highly advisable to schedule this session as soon as possible after the family's admission for treatment. A second family art evaluation is scheduled after about six months or at discharge to assess the changes that have occurred.

As in family art therapy, another person takes part in the evaluation sessions. We call him *participant observer* rather than *cotherapist* because these sessions are focused on diagnosis rather than on therapy. His role is therefore to observe and note what is going on in the family during the family art evaluation; these observations may later be referred to in the course of verbal family therapy. The participant observer (always a person involved in the treatment of the particular family) may also make some immediate relevant remarks and comments. The degree of his active participation depends on his personal inclination. However, the instructions to the family are given exclusively by the art therapist.

The average time needed for the evaluation session of a family of four or five is one and one half to two hours; there is no firm time limit, as there is in the therapy sessions. In my experience, however, we had small families who took up to three hours for the same tasks done by larger families in much less time, although usually large families would be expected to take longer. Indeed, speed of performance provides clues about a family's way of functioning. Slowness may be a sign of resistance manifested by using excessive time on each picture. Slowness in getting started or an obsessive preoccupation with details is often unconsciously aimed at cutting down the time available for discussion of the art product. This situation is sometimes hard for the art therapist to handle. When someone appears to be engrossed in an art experience, it is not easy to urge him to finish or tell him to stop. Here the art therapist needs tact; at one and the same time he must show appreciation of the individual's efforts, yet let him know that these prolonged efforts must be drawn to a close as quickly as possible.

It might, of course, be valuable to discuss with the family what lies behind such slowness. But any such comment should preferably be made by the participant observer, who treats the family, rather than by the art therapist, for whom it is the first and often the only encounter with the family.

Upon arrival in the interview room, families sometimes express uneasiness when they see the art equipment. The art therapist must emphasize that the purpose of the session is not to test their artistic skills, but that they use these simple art media as a means of communication and self-expression. Little more explanation is given; the family members are encouraged to start and see for themselves what it is all about.

The attitude of the art therapist must be supportive and friendly, but also firm. No help of any kind, such as adjustment of easels or further explanation of the procedures, is given to younger children until the parents or siblings have responded (or not responded) to the child's plea for help. Their behavior in this regard is an important source of information about how the parents have met the needs of their adolescent or young adult offspring in their early childhood.

In contrast to family art therapy, where a variety of art media is offered, in family art evaluation only semihard square-edged pastels are used, for the following reasons: (1) The type of pastels recommended is quick and easy to use; it presents no technical problems, as might dripping paint, crumbling clay, etc. (2) For the sake of obtaining accurate research material, the use of a uniform medium is imperative; different media may influence the character of the art product and confuse the data.

PROCEDURES

As mentioned earlier, the majority of the procedures of the family art evaluation stem from the most significant themes that have recurred through the years in the pictures spontaneously drawn by patients and families. I have devised a few additional techniques with the goal of highlighting the families' patterns of communication and interaction. Some of the procedures (comparison of the first and last pictures of the series and the use of scribble pictures) are similar to a method devised by Elinor Ulman and described in her article "A New Use of Art in Psychiatric Diagnosis."[18] Her exquisite sensitivity and broad experience allowed her to provide important diagnostic conclusions drawn from four tasks given to the patients investigated individually; (1) a picture of their own choice; (2) a broad scribble on paper; (3) a picture started with the help of a scribble; (4) a final picture either freely chosen or derived from a scribble.

In my method the drawings that are requested in the family art evaluation are:

1. A free picture.*
2. A picture of your family.
3. An abstract family portrait.
4. A picture started with the help of a scribble.
5. A joint family scribble.
6. A free picture.

The sequence of tasks in the family art evaluation is important. The family is gradually led from complete freedom in their choice of subject to more structured, increasingly stress-producing procedures. At the highest level of stress (after Procedure 3, abstract family portrait), body movement is introduced (exercise before Procedure 4, which will be described in detail below) to release the tension without interrupting the session and the sequence of tasks.

The last task is again the picture of a subject freely chosen.

---

*A *free picture* is one for which no subject is assigned; the patient and his family may draw whatever they wish.

By comparing the last free picture with the first free picture, we learn about how family members have been able to handle the stress of the entire session. It also often carries the most important message.

After each procedure is completed, family members usually comment spontaneously on each other's pictures. When the family is apathetic or withdrawn, the art therapist may need to suggest that they look together at each picture. We usually do not push much in this direction after the first procedure. We want to help the family to adjust to this new situation and become as comfortable as possible. However, if the family remains very reserved during the first procedure but we notice something especially striking in any of their pictures, we do not hesitate to focus the family's attention on it and encourage further discussion.

In Procedure 1, the first free picture, each member of the family is asked to "draw a picture of whatever comes to mind." It is emphasized that they are not expected to make elaborate drawings because quite a number of pictures will have to be drawn.

In Procedure 2, the family portrait, each member of the family is asked to take a fresh sheet of paper and to "draw a picture of your family, each member of the family including yourself. We do not expect you to make very elaborate photographic portraits. Do the best you can; there is no right or wrong. We would also like you to draw the whole person." If a question is asked about whom to include and whom not to include (for instance, a married family member or an absent family member), the answer is, "Whatever way you choose to do it."

Despite the initial instruction, the family at times asks again if we want the whole body or just the face. In this case we say that we would like them to make the whole person, but we put no pressure on them; their eventual choice of what to represent may be revealing. After they have finished, they are asked to label each family member with the person's name, to give general titles to their pictures, and to sign and date them. (This request is made in all procedures.)

Pictures of the family usually stimulate spontaneous discussion; if they do not, we again try to call attention to something particularly striking we have noticed but upon which no one has commented. After the discussion ends, the family is asked to change the sheet of paper and the third procedure is explained.

Procedure 3, abstract family portrait, is the most difficult to explain. We have found that the best way to begin is to ask that each member of the family draw an abstract family portrait and wait for their questions. How the families react to this task will be described in more detail when examples will be presented.

After the family has finished this procedure, spontaneous discussion usually ensues because each person wants to know the meaning of a particular symbol by which he is represented. If this does not happen, we try to start the discussion by saying, "I think that these pictures require some explanation." Then we wait for awhile. Sometimes the family members go from one picture to another and ask each other very interesting questions. At other times they remain withdrawn and it may be necessary to suggest that they look at each picture one by one. This last step should be avoided if possible because it interferes with spontaneous interactional patterns.

As with the first family portraits, they are asked to identify by name each person represented, give their portraits general titles, and sign and date them. The abstract family portraits are usually the most time-consuming but also the most interesting of all the procedures; they bring up many highly charged feelings and are the climactic point of the session. This is why relaxing body exercises are introduced immediately following them in preparation for the individual scribble drawing.

In Procedure 4, a picture started with the help of a scribble, the family members are invited to stand up, to take a piece of pastel in their hands, and to do arm exercises as demonstrated by the art therapist. These movements, besides relieving tension, are aimed at physically loosening up and enhancing freedom of motion in the scribbles they will later make.[13] First we ask them to draw in the air long straight vertical lines, swinging their arms up and down from the shoulder. Next they are asked to repeat the free-swinging movement horizontally in order to make straight horizontal lines. Finally we ask them to make big circles in the air; we emphasize that the motion should come from the whole body. Then we ask them to do a broad free-floating scribble in the air, using the same kinds of movement; again, the art therapist does this scribble in the air with them. At this point they are asked to go immediately to their easels, close their eyes in order not to restrict and consciously guide the scribble, and do the same type of scribble on the paper already prepared. Despite these uniform preliminaries, the style and character of the scribble vary a great deal from one person to another and from one family to another.

After the scribble has been made, we ask the family members to look at their scribbles and see if they can discern anything in them that reminds them of something they could use as the start of their pictures. They may turn their boards any way they wish, so that any side may become the bottom of the picture. Then, if they have seen something and can decide on it as a subject, we ask them to go ahead and draw the picture on the same piece of paper, using the initial scribble as a stimulus for choosing a subject to develop into a picture. We emphasize that they may add as many lines and shapes to the scribble lines as they wish and ignore as many as they wish.

If the family still does not understand, we use the following comparison: "Have you ever watched the clouds in the sky and seen different cloud formations that remind you of animals, people, landscapes, and so on? Well, this is about the same thing." As in other procedures, after each family member has drawn his own picture started from the scribble, we ask for a title, signature and date.

In Procedure 5, joint family scribble, we repeat the same instructions as for the individual scribble. But after each has completed his own scribble, we ask them to look together at all the scribbles and tell each other what they see at first glance in each or any of them. They are to choose one scribble to use as the basis of a joint picture after having decided together what they see in it. They have to agree on the final choice of the subject and then draw it together, all working on just one of the scribbles. We interfere as little as possible, leaving the family on their own as to how they will carry out this particular transaction. They are also asked to decide jointly on the title and on how they are going to sign the picture.

Comparison on the scribble pictures done individually with those done by the family group offers particularly rich data. Does the family yield to the psychopathology of the more sick family member or are they able to stand against it? Depending on the answer to this question, the joint picture may become more bizarre and disjointed than the individual ones; on the other hand, it may present more unity and integration.

The sixth and last procedure is again a free picture, no subject assigned. The family is asked to do exactly the same thing as at the beginning: "Draw a picture of whatever comes to mind." As pointed out, after completing each picture, individual or joint, families are asked to sign, title and date their pictures. The insistence on the title and signature is not without reason. The title is significant because of its relevance or irrelevance to the subject drawn, because of its idiosyncratic meaning, or because it is excessively concrete or carries an additional symbolic meaning.

The following examples will demonstrate what the therapist and the family can learn about family dynamics, perceptions and relations in a single art evaluation session.

First Procedure: Free Picture

Even though no such request is made, the first picture frequently turns out to be an individual's introduction of himself or may present the family problem. The latter occurs more often in neurotic than in schizophrenic families, where problems are diffuse and less clearly defined. The two following pictures can serve as examples.

Figure 32, "Home, Sweet Home," by Sue, a thirteen-year-old girl, was the first picture done at a preadmission session in which the family art evaluation procedures were used to determine whether family art therapy was the treatment of choice for this family. Sue and her sixteen-year-old brother Gary were both underachievers; their school performance was far below their potential, and their continuing failure prompted the family to seek treatment.

Figure 32.

The financial situation in this family was quite difficult. The father had to work seventy to eighty hours a week to earn enough to sustain them. In this picture we see him leaving for his evening job, saying, "Good dinner, got to leave for work now." Gary also leaves to go his own way; "See you," he says.

The mother, "Mom," a tense, tired woman shown at the upper left, is torn between the two younger children. The baby cries in his crib; Mom says, "Got to feed the baby." Jean, the eight-year-old, is sitting on the floor and making another demand: "Mom, can I have something to eat?" Sue, on the far left, stands with arms helplessly extended, saying, "Just a minute and I'll do my homework."

Later in this session Sue burst into tears and explained through her sobs how she felt that she had to help her exhausted mother with the housework and the baby and then was too tired to do her homework. The sarcastic title of the picture carries the bitterness this child feels about her home.

Figure 33, the first picture by Sue's father, presents his view of the state of affairs in the family. Like Sue's, it is a cartoon-like drawing, but cruder than hers. Nevertheless, it poignantly carries his distress and isolation. Only two stick figures, "Mom" and "Dad," are represented. "Mom" is surrounded by wavy lines inscribed, "Tired, finances, children, baby, headache, housework." The inscription "Sea of problems" points toward this part of the drawing. On the other side, "Dad" is seen isolated on an "Island," reaching, however, toward "Mom."

Figure 33.

It is interesting that he excluded the children from this picture, making it clear that the core of the problem is between the spouses. When discussing the picture, he added the observation that their relationship reflected upon the children and was the reason for their poor grades. Dealing with the depression of the mother and the helpless isolation of the father became, therefore, the focal objective of treatment.

These freely drawn first pictures often also provide a diagnostic impression of individual family members. The art therapist is frequently not informed who the identified patient in the family is. However, he often has a chance to obtain diagnostic clues from the very beginning of the evaluation session.

For instance, Figures 34 and 35 were made by twenty-five-year-old twin sisters Janet and Jenny. I had had no prior contact with the family and knew nothing about their history and psychopathology. I also did not know whether one, both or neither of the twins was schizophrenic.

Figure 34.

At the family art evaluation session, neither of these twins exhibited psychotic behavior; both presented a facade of good adjustment. Both drew landscapes related to their homes. The first impression was that of representations fairly well-organized and complete, even if naively primitive. Upon closer scrutiny, however, one perceives differences that immediately throw light on the psychopathology of one of the sisters, Janet.

Janet said that Figure 34 was her own yard and that she was homesick for it. She called attention to the patio, the fence, the roses, and so on. She added a rainbow of a most unrealistic shape. When asked to give a title to the picture, she wrote a list of all the elements she had drawn, "rainbow in the sky, birds, sun, fence, roses, patio, pine tree," but she had lost the meaning of the whole

Figure 35

picture and failed to indicate its emotional content; she had reduced it to a bunch of fragments.

Her sister Jenny, on the other hand, drew a complex, somewhat incongruous landscape (Fig. 35). She first called it "Farm
House." Then, for more exactness, she said that it did not truly
represent a farm and changed the title to "Country Scene." She
tried, through her search for an appropriate title, to relate the
elements to each other, seeking by this means to attain greater
coherence.

The organization of each sister's thinking processes was clearly
displayed; after the first ten minutes, I had some reason to believe
that Janet was the schizophrenic patient. This was confirmed by
the succeeding procedures and was in accordance with what I
later learned of her history and preadmission diagnosis.

As we see, the first procedure can already serve a useful diagnostic purpose. Through their pictures and in the use they make
of them, we can note the degree of psychopathology of different
family members without being biased by other information about

them. Our findings may reinforce, or conversely, may raise questions about tentative diagnostic impressions other investigators obtained from different sources and procedures.

Second Procedure: Family Portrait

This procedure originated from the frequent spontaneous depiction by family members of each other in family art therapy sessions. I would like to stress the difference between this assignment and similar tasks given in psychological testing or in individual or group therapy, in which patients are often told, "Draw your family."

When these tasks are given in a one-to-one situation, the communication is obviously restricted to the person who does the drawing and the tester or the therapist. In group art therapy the communication extends to the rest of the group. Group members may eventually respond to family portraits by others as being projections of their own family relationships and share with the group similar personal feelings.

Drawing family members in their presence, however, elicits reactions and insights not possible in other therapeutic situations. Not only the person who draws the other but also other family members present are engaged in an important relationship with each other. These portraits open the way to all family members for clarification and better understanding of roles, relationships and perceptions of each other.

It is worth mentioning another difference between material obtained in testing and that obtained in art therapy or evaluation. In art therapy we supply color and large sheets of paper, affording the possibility to accentuate more vividly characteristics of the persons represented, thus providing richer, more diversified portrayals. Contrary to *Family Kinetic Drawings*,[19] we never specify whether we expect a picture of the family in action. Therefore we obtain a true depiction of how the family members see the family's customary interaction. We obtain a variety of types of family portraits—an alignment of family members similar to that found in a rogues' gallery, without any connection with each other, or even drawn in separate compartments, or a picture of a family engaged in a joint activity. In the latter case, we can surmise that the family does not see itself as a number of isolated persons, but that the sharing of activities or interests is a habitual pattern of their daily life. In both types of representations we can notice pairing, distancing or isolation of family members.

We have already had some examples of portraits of family members emerging spontaneously from scribbles (Figs. 4 and 16). Of those described below, however, the first was planned as a portrait of a member of the family group, and the second was subsequently recognized as a family member present at the session.

A mother, Mrs. Kernay, said she wanted to portray "my daughter, my beautiful daughter." Nadine, her only daughter, a twenty-year-old schizophrenic girl, was totally dependent on her. She was unable to make any decision without her mother's approval. She would call her mother from the hospital in the morning asking what she should wear, what she should do, and so on.

Mrs. Kernay became disturbed and annoyed when she saw that the figure she had drawn looks "juvenile" (Fig. 36). "This is the little girl. . . . She is my little girl. . . . Her body is all wrong." She sought help and support from me, but when I advised her to look at her daughter while drawing her, Mrs. Kernay replied, "I don't have to look at her because I know how she looks. . . . I want her to smile." The daughter asked, "It that me?" and got the answer, "No, that's my other girl."

This picture and the mother's remarks provided an excellent opportunity to point out Mrs. Kernay's distorted view of her daughter. She could not bear to see her daughter as an adult. She preserved in her mind the image of "my little girl, my other little girl," the happy, smiling child she still wished to have.

The discussion of this picture helped make Mrs. Kernay aware of her distorted view of her daughter, of her reluctance to see her as grown and to let her go. On the other hand, the daughter gained some understanding of her acceptance of the role thrust upon her by her mother and of her own reluctance to grow up.

In another family, the father drew "A Girl" (Fig. 37). While drawing this picture, he was saying, "I am going to draw a girl, no particular girl. . . . Looks like a fifty-five-year-old woman. . . .

Figure 36.

Looks like a battle-ax, doesn't it?" Sammy, the son in this family and the identified patient, exclaimed, "It looks like Mom!" The mother asked, "Like who, like who?" Sammy repeated, "Like you!" The father was delighted, but retracted, "The way the face and the features came out is purely accidental [laughs]. I started out drawing a girl, but I see it's a. . . ." The mother then said seriously, "Yes, that's right . . . maybe it looks like me."

Actually "The Girl" does strikingly resemble this mother, a domineering, angry woman. The family recognized and delighted in the hostile image made by the father. Strangely enough, no

Figure 37.

one seemed to feel guilty or hurt. The mutual and open recognition and acceptance of the feelings projected through this picture opened the way to work on them further in verbal conjoint family therapy.

Occurrences such as these led us to decide to include family portraits in the evaluative procedures we developed later. Let us look now at some of these family portraits, drawn as a requested task in the second procedure of the family art evaluation.

Figure 38 was drawn by a twenty-three-year-old male patient who displayed the kind of disorganized behavior that easily identified him as schizophrenic. In this picture the enormous mother almost appears to be carrying the tiny father in her arms. Other family members are slightly larger than the father and, like him, helplessly extend their arms into space. The only exception is a sister who is drawn in profile and turned toward the patient. I later learned that though she was much more successful and better adjusted than her brother, she shared his tendency to worry and was closer to him than anyone else in the family was. It was not difficult to infer the parental roles in the family.

Figure 39 is another family portrait. It was produced by a twenty-two-year-old male schizophrenic patient during an acute psychotic episode. In family psychotherapy sessions as well as during the family art evaluation, he constantly attacked his mother. Here we see a paranoid view of the mother's malignant influence on all family members. They are all tied to her; she directs them by means of electrodes implanted in their brains, reducing them to marionettes on strings. The patient, on the lower right, is the one who accuses; in a mixture of French and schizophrenese, he designates her as the evil one.

Figure 38.

Figure 39.

It may look as if these two patients made distorted portraits because of their own oedipal or other problems centered on the parent depicted. In both instances, however, the bizarre representations merely magnify the real role and personality of the mother, in each case a domineering, castrating female, as was shown more and more clearly throughout the session both by her behavior and by the family's art productions.

Third Procedure: Abstract Family Portrait

This procedure is not easy even for well-integrated individuals or families. Nevertheless, I introduced it into family art evaluation because it gives reliable information about each person's capacity for organized abstract thinking. The samples we obtain frequently depict concrete objects used as symbols, such as objects related to people's occupations or hobbies. Less often, we obtain true abstractions in which colors and shapes alone convey a meaning. In the families of schizophrenics, usually not only the designated patient but also most of the other family members make concrete rather than abstract representations. In both normal and less disturbed families, more often family members can grasp and represent an abstract idea.

Here I would like to turn again to the evolution of the evaluative procedures.

Figure 40.

Figure 40 is a picture drawn, beginning with a scribble, by the mother of an eighteen-year-old schizophrenic girl, Sharon. She called it "A Baby in Bunting." At first she connected it with her grandchild, but then she exclaimed, "It might be that I never can think of Sharon as a grown-up person. . . . I always think she is still a baby in bunting."

Sharon responded by painting a very impressive abstraction (Plate IX), which she explained as follows: "The central form is a powerful mother with eight children, still unformed, all but two [the one on the top and the other on the left] cut off from her." We see the masses of blue wavy shapes encircling the other children. Sharon was outspoken about her feelings that children should go their own way and be separated from their mothers. The two children not yet separated were herself and her younger brother; the oldest brother was married and had cut himself off from the powerful mother.

This painting beautifully depicts family relations in an abstract manner and gave us the idea for the evaluative procedure that we call abstract family portrait.

The range of abstractness in these family portraits is very broad. Through the years we came to recognize that people in certain diagnostic categories interpreted this task in similar ways.

How is this task explained to the family? As with all the procedures, we try to start with exactly the same directions for all families. In this case it is especially important because the family's response might be influenced if the therapist's explanation of the task were not kept uniformly simple. This is a particularly important point if the material obtained is to be used for diagnosis or for systematic analysis for research.

So we simply say, "Now we would like you to draw an abstract family portrait." A number of people understand the task and require no more explanation. This, of course, depends on the level of sophistication, which in turn is related to educational and socioeconomic class. For persons acquainted with trends in modern art, our request does not present much of a puzzle, and they may start to work on their pictures without comment or request for explanation. However, this readiness and apparent understanding often does not exclude very concrete depictions of personalities, revealing the family's characteristic style of thinking.

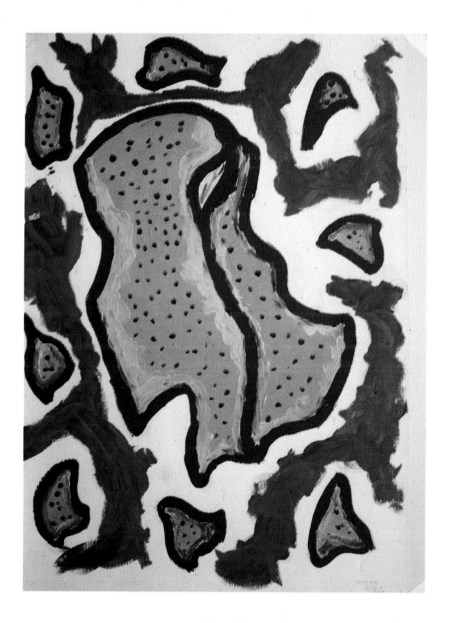

Plate IX.

Plate X.

But family members unfamiliar with the concept of abstract art look at us in amazement after our initial request and ask, "What do you mean?" In such instances we turn the question back to them, asking what they think we mean in order to elicit their concept of an abstract portrait. Often people ask whether we mean portraits that are "distorted" or are "caricatures" or "cartoons." Other families come closer to understanding that different colors and shapes are to be used to represent personalities of the family members.

After hearing all the responses, we give our own definition: "Now don't draw bodies and faces as you just did, but use color, motion, lines and shapes to depict the personality, the way you feel about or see each member of your family, including yourself."

Family members sometimes ask further questions, but usually they go ahead with their drawings. Some examples of how the abstract portraits are understood follow.

Symbols of Hobbies or Occupations

This is the kind of abstract portrait made most by borderline or obsessive-compulsive individuals. It is easier and less threatening to represent what a person does than what a person is or how the person drawing the picture feels about him. So we see, for example, a stove for mother "because she cooks," a guitar for brother "because he likes to play," a chair for father "because he sits and reads the newspaper," and "a TV for me because I like to watch TV."

Not much abstraction here, but in spite of that, it gives us an idea of what the home life of this family is.

Meaningless Symbolism of Colors and Shapes

Sometimes we see abstractions in which persons are depicted by colors and shapes that do not carry any emotional meaning. They may be generalized: "I drew father in gray because men wear gray suits." Or they may be more personal but unrelated to feelings or mood. A red blob for mother would then be explained, "Mother looks well in red"; a blue square for brother "because he is wearing a blue sweater today."

The drawings by themselves may carry some vague symbolic messages, but the individual's defenses exclude the possible threat of recognizing and expressing feelings and reduce the picture to a concrete, meaningless statement. Individuals with schizoid personalities and families of schizophrenics are likely to respond in this fashion to this task.

Expressive Use of Abstract Symbols

Plates X and XI, abstract family portraits, are impressive and demonstrate how dramatically this procedure can convey and express intense feelings about family relations. But we must note a subtle difference between the identified patient's picture and her sister's.

Babs, the patient, at age twelve started to be preoccupied with her uneasiness about boys and dating. She also became more and more upset by her parents' frequent fights. Her disturbance gradually grew into overwhelming panic, feelings of depersonalization, and suicidal impulses. The school psychologist advised psychiatric treatment, and, as her symptoms increased, she was briefly hospitalized. Later, because of Babs' increasing involvement in the family problems, family therapy on an outpatient basis was recommended as the most suitable treatment.

Babs' diagnosis was adolescent adjustment reaction with hysterical and depressive features; there was some concern about a schizophrenic pattern, but psychological tests did not show thought disorder.

Upon admission for treatment, the parents, Babs, (then seventeen) and her two sisters, Wanda (nineteen) and Helen (eleven) were seen in a family art evaluation session. Babs explained her dramatic abstract family portrait (Plate X) as follows: "There is a symbol for each person. . . . On the left, that's Helen—a riding cap and a crop. Here is a golf club and a golf bag [on right]." She did not identify these as representing her father until she was asked by the psychiatrist participant-observer.

"This is a hand of cards, bridge cards, clubs, diamonds, hearts; this is my mother." Then, pointing at the two shapes at the bottom, "And you will find a link here—a book and a record—this

Plate XI.

Plate XII.

is classical music or blues; this is Wanda . . . And I. . . . This is
me." ". . . This is a heart; the heart per se represents the family."
Asked by the father what the colors mean, she answered, "The
black is predominant, of course. This is the conflict here. This is
part of the family, these lines here, black" (indicating the strong,
crosslike central figure).

The father, obviously upset by the somber and threatening
atmosphere of the picture, attempted to find something less dark
and dramatic in it. "You have some yellow." But Babs insisted,
"This is part of the conflict."

What is particularly striking in this picture is that the concrete symbols representing the family members are obscured,
practically obliterated, by the gigantic cross over them. It also
crosses out the heart-family.

The two large unexpected shapes at the top of the cross look
like two angry faces attacking one another. Although they were
not acknowledged as such in words, we cannot but think of the
parental fights, especially after hearing Wanda's explanation of
her picture.

Plate XI is Wanda's abstract family portrait. She explained,

> Mine is symbolic. Things are kind of pretty wild. I had to think
> of something that would express what I feel and that's I . . . nature.
> Dad is up there and he is the sun. Mom is the moon. They have a
> fight trying to decide who will take over. Babs and I are down there
> under and are deciding whether to stay alive and . . . there is Helen.
> She doesn't really; she is more safe than anyone. She is somehow out
> of the picture and she is growing very well.

Wanda also focused on the destructive parental conflict, but
even though she turned to "nature" to express it, the symbols she
used do not have the concreteness of the purely occupational
symbols used by Babs, which she eventually obliterated by the
overwhelming conflict.

Wanda's representation is easier for us to understand and to
respond to. We can see the two sister-plants, wilting and bending
under the destructive influence of the battle between the planets
that stand for the parents. Helen, as yet untouched by the fighting, is separate, blooming happily. We notice that in Babs' picture Helen also seems to be untouched by the conflict.

Although both pictures convey a similar message, the subtle difference in the manner in which it is represented makes us reflect upon the difference in the sisters' thinking processes. Some of the suspected schizoid patterns in Babs' thinking may be suggested by the concreteness of her symbols. On the other hand, hysteric features are even more evident in the overdramatization of the conflict, which has been magnified to the point that it obliterates everything else. The predominance of black and the reluctance to use colors indicate a depressive tendency.

Fourth Procedure: Individual Scribble

Various examples of pictures developed individually from scribbles were given in preceding chapters. In addition to their usefulness as an instrument for diagnosing individual family members, when compared with the joint family scribble, they also help in the understanding of some of the family dynamics.

Fifth Procedure: The Joint Family Scribble
and Its Diagnostic Implication

This procedure was described earlier in this chapter, but some clinical examples will give us a better understanding of its very special value, as much diagnostically as dynamically.

We saw in Figure 27 a joint scribble by the Williams family that is typical of the response to this assignment on the part of a family with chronic schizophrenic offspring.

Figure 41, a joint scribble by the Hilton family, brings us another sample of the results of this procedure. In this family, the seventeen-year-old daughter Rose, the identified patient, was a chronic process schizophrenic with amorphous, poorly differentiated forms of thinking.

The parents, Rose, and her twelve-year-old brother, John, participated in the session. John was not overtly psychotic, but his mannerisms and gesticulations were frequently infantile and bizarre, and his art productions indicated extremely low self-esteem combined with frequent impulses toward violence and destruction.

The picture is called both "A Hershey Kisses" and "A

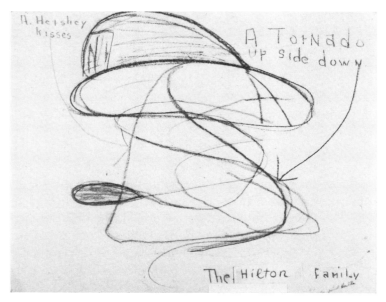

Figure 41.

Tornado upside down." During its production, the Hilton family was extremely active and showered us with associations. They switched from one scribble to another, unable to settle on anything. John pointed out a big nose and a boomerang and finally outlined in red on his father's scribble what he called "A Hershey Kisses." His father accepted this title and wrote it on the sheet, but they continued to work on the picture. The patient saw a balloon and then outlined an "S" for a snake; the mother saw the shape of a fireman's hat. The father brought up a childhood memory of being scared by "a snake with a wide open mouth in a strawberry patch." This association shows how primary process material is brought into the open through the scribble procedure. The mother at first protested that the things the family saw in the scribble did not make sense with each other. But finally she gave in to the irrationality of the group and outlined in black what she had earlier identified as a fireman's hat. As if encouraged by her capitulation, the rest of the family continued to make irrelevant additions to the picture. John drew a letter "A" in blue; the patient, another "S." Then suddenly John said he saw a tornado. The mother again remarked on the bizarreness of the picture and pronounced it a little disjointed but let her objections go and joined the others, outlining another letter "A." The confusion in the family grew.

John's excited exclamations added to the chaos in the picture itself. "A tornado upside down! Here are the Hershey Kisses, chocolate tornado upside down! An arrow pointing to it! I love chocolate tornadoes!"

It is worth noting that, like the father in the Williams family, the mother did not use her actual common sense in dealing with the family's irrationality but let herself be swayed by the mass confusion. We have observed in a number of families that the offspring are consistently more severely ill when both parents contribute passively or actively to the family transactional disorder than if one takes a stand against the confusion or at least refrains from taking part in it.*

In contrast to the examples above, Figure 42, "Someone We Miss," shows us that this family endeavor can not only be well organized and integrated but can also express a deep emotion shared by the whole family. This picture was developed from a scribble by a family referred for treatment because of the four-teen-year-old son's failure in school despite his high IQ. The family agreed promptly that they saw a lady in a rocking chair; this led by association to the recently deceased grandmother, loved and missed by all of them.

A further important function of the joint scribble in family art evaluation is that by comparing it with the individual pictures derived from scribbles, we can observe the impact of the psychopathology of the more sick family member on the total family group. Is there an inherent strength in the family that enables them to resist irrationality and distortion and to organize the joint picture into a meaningful whole, or is the patient left in control of the transaction? Will a picture done jointly by some of the family members become more or less integrated, more or less expressive, depending on the presence or absence of a particular family member?

*From Hanna Yaxa Kwiatkowska. The use of families art productions for psychiatric evaluation. *Bulletin of Art Therapy, 6*(2):52-69, 1967.

Figure 42.

Figure 43.

Figure 44.

Three pictures, Figures 43, 44 and 45, give us an idea of some of the things that may happen.

Twenty-year-old Patsy Welston's problems could be traced to early childhood, but around age fifteen her symptoms became so acute that they could no longer be ignored or denied by her parents. Her gradual deterioration led to several short hospitalizations. Some of these were ended by her father's having her discharged against medical advice. For a time she would stay at home, settling down to an essentially psychotic level of compensation. In her acute periods of frankly psychotic behavior, she

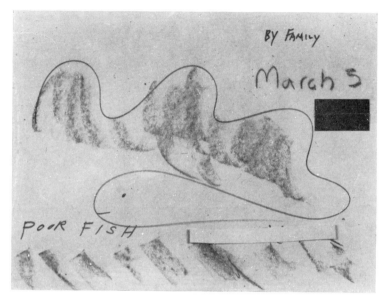

Figure 45.

would hallucinate and at times become violent. In both phases she would exhibit disruptive behavior, peculiar mannerisms, inappropriate giggling, and overt pseudosexual, oral and narcissistic preoccupation with genitals. Her appearance and clothing were most bizarre. Her diagnosis was chronic undifferentiated schizophrenia.

Mr. Welston, a well-to-do real estate broker, came from a large family with whom he was still very entangled; two of his sisters were schizophrenic. Mrs. Welston was the most intact member of the family and could see what was going on but could not do anything about it. Renée, Patsy's twenty-one-year-old sister, was quite involved in the family's difficulties and their struggles with Patsy's disruptive behavior but had managed to go through adolescence functioning adequately, both scholastically and socially.

In this family mother was clearly aligned with Renée, and father with Patsy. To some extent Mr. Welston allowed his daughters to act out with him their oedipal wishes. His relationship with Patsy was almost openly incestuous, while with Renée it was more clandestine. Renée's covert competition with her sister for their father's favors, otherwise denied by her, was clearly manifested in her pictures.[21] Patsy responded to her father's attitude by making unending irrational demands on him. Mr. Welston yielded to them all in the belief that this would "help her to get well."

The pictures to follow were drawn both in family art therapy and at a second family art evaluation session held at the end of treatment. The former are included because they too help illuminate joint family transactions.

Figure 43, "The Goast" (as Patsy spelled it) was painted jointly by Mr. Welston and Patsy in a family art therapy session. The rest of the family was present but did not take part in the drawing of this magnificently crazy picture with many apparently disconnected elements. Let us look at it more closely.

The curved track with what he called a "chug-chug train" is a frequent theme in Mr. Welston's pictures, a fantasy of escaping with Patsy to a solitary place where, under his care, she would "get well." We see these items on the left. We can recognize Patsy's usual style in the bizarre figures at the bottom of the picture: the defecating animal and other grotesque figures. The row of elongated objects in the center was explained by Patsy as "lollipops," which appear to be a regressive expression of her infantile oral needs. However, the whole picture is fascinating and exciting, and we felt it to be full of private meaning—a communication between father and daughter, fully understandable only to them.

The mother's contribution was confined to the suggestion that the picture be titled "The Ghost." Through this label she seemed to try to make sense out of the totally crazy picture.

Figure 44, made by the father and the two daughters in the mother's absence, was started with the help of a scribble. Here we see that the older sister gave in to the style established by father and Patsy. The resulting picture is ugly and bizarre, mainly restricted to the original lines of the scribble, not integrated. If we compare it with Figure 43, we notice that it lacks the thrilling excitement that impressed us in "The Goast." It is somewhat constricted, as if Renée's presence had a stifling effect on the *folie à deux* enjoyed by Patsy and her father.

Figure 45 is the joint family scribble drawn at the final family art evaluation before Patsy's discharge. She was very restless and kept moving in and out of the room. She would not participate in any of the suggested procedures. This joint scribble was made by the parents and Renée while Patsy was out in the hall.

Here we see a total change of style. The picture has a certain unity and does not shock us by being uncanny or disturbing. However, it impresses us as empty and fails to catch our interest or stimulate our imagination. In contrast, Figure 43, even though not understandable to us, has buoyancy and life.

Its title, "Poor Fish," is significant. It was suggested by mother and accepted enthusiastically by father and Renée. Our first thought was that the "poor fish" might represent Patsy. However, the family's restrained comments led us to think that possibly each of them identified with the "poor fish." A simplistic way to look at it would be that the "poor fish"—mother, father or Renée—was caught in the sea of Patsy's problems. But when we look at what Patsy's participation brought into the joint pictures, we cannot but wonder if the "poor fish" here is not deploring Patsy's absence, which left them feeling deprived of the excitement Patsy brought into their lives. It would seem that her craziness provided a sort of cover that allowed the others to express unconscious wishes and fantasies.

Sixth Procedure: Free Picture

The final procedure, like the first, a free picture, has proved to be one of the most enlightening and seems to sum up the family's total experience.

The difference between the first and last pictures can be defined as a measure of each family member's tolerance of the stress aroused by the uncovering aspect of the preceding art procedures. These procedures are so designed that they usually stimulate the expressive powers of the stable individual; however, they are likely to be felt as a menace by a person whose ego is more vulnerable.

With the psychotic individual, the last picture is apt to be more disorganized than the first, while the work of a person able to mobilize his defenses is likely to become more rigidly controlled and constricted.

The last picture of the evaluation series is certainly very useful in diagnosis, but I attribute even more importance to the ultimate personal message it often transmits. Obviously, the participants have agreed to go through the family art evaluation because they are in trouble and seek treatment. But at the same time the experience is new to them; they are unclear about what their attitudes should be. It is easy for them to take it as a game; often we hear that it reminds people of "the first grade." Especially in families where the designated patient is neurotic rather than psychotic, with problems centered around adjustment to adolescence, we see a tendency to cover anxiety by giggling, joking and refusing to recognize meaning in the pictures. But under this cover a lot of emotions are inevitably stirred.

The empathic attitude of the therapists in accepting even the crudest of their pictures, and even more, the peculiar power of expression through art, cannot fail to bring about a gradual change in the atmosphere of the session and the attitude of the family. Except with frankly paranoid or overanxious families, the relationship with the art therapist toward the end of the session is friendly, at times even warm. Material carefully avoided throughout the session may appear in the last picture, bringing an important message of trust, as opposed to a defensive, rigid last picture by others.

Such a positive change is illustrated by a dramatic picture, Figure 46, drawn by Justin, a husky fourteen-year-old boy, the youngest of three children. The family had sought treatment in an emergency. In reaction to his mother's reprimand for sneaking into the house at 3:00 AM, Justin had punched his eighteen-year-old sister in the face, breaking her nose. This was the culmination of a series of delinquent acts that included breaking into a building in order to steal. Justin threatened that any time his mother nagged him he would beat up his sister again.

The family art evaluation took place a few days after the incident. When the family arrived, Myrna, the sister, looked tragi-comic, with symmetrical panda-like black and blue bruises under her eyes and a painfully swollen nose that was still too sore for plastic surgery. We had expected an angry, sullen group, but to our astonishment the family was quite cooperative and animated. However, one could sense that underneath the joviality they were steering clear of anything related to Justin's behavior and other family difficulties. We noticed in the pictures many significant clues to the complicated Justin-Myrna-mother triangle, but none of these was recognized by the family. In addition, little color was used; pictures were drawn mainly in black or in faded drab colors, indicating general underlying depression.

Justin initially tried to fall in with the family's pseudojovial behavior, appearing self-assured, even defiant, but as the session progressed he withdrew more and more. Toward the end he was a pathetic little figure, huddled in his chair, completely cut off from the others, immersed in his own world.

His last picture, Figure 46, was a poignant message of his need for help if tragedy was to be averted. The figure lying on the railroad track and screaming "Help" was designated by Justin as "someone." But when we look at the upper left where he signed his name, we find above it the word "Help" again; this time the plea is direct: "Help Justin." It is highly improbable that Justin would have been able to speak about his distress and need for help as early in psychotherapeutic treatment. In other pread-mission interviews he showed no sign of emotion and maintained a boldly detached attitude.

In another case a mother's last picture revealed the family's unresolved grief and mourning for the deceased father. The Bogden family had been referred for treatment because of the psychosomatic symptoms of the younger son, Johnny. He suffered severe abdominal pains for which no physical origin could be found. There were no behavioral problems; at school he was de-scribed as a "pleasant young man who enjoys school," although his performance was rather low, especially in reading. Mr. Bogden had died six years before; the mother's remarriage was annulled after a year. Apparently the new husband did not fulfill mother's

Figure 46.

expectations of a father for her sons.

The family art evaluation session was unusually dull. The mother and sons remained remote from the therapists and were mostly engaged in private exchanges audible only to each other. The one significant message conveyed by the pictures lay in the complete absence of the deceased parent and of an older, married brother from all family portraits. The therapists felt depressed and discouraged; the observers behind the one-way mirror were bored.

Then came the "Wishing Well" (Fig. 47), the last picture drawn by the mother. When I asked Mrs. Bogden what she would

Figure 47.

wish if she tossed a coin in the well, Johnny quickly exclaimed, "I know!" Mrs. Bogden continued then in a low voice, "My wish would be that they find a cure for cancer; my husband, their father, died of cancer." Johnny immediately whispered, "I knew she would say that." The older brother joined, saying with feeling, "I would wish for the same thing."

In this case again the essence of the family's problem was revealed in the last picture after an apparently barren and frustrating session. This revelation of unresolved loss and mourning, with all the implications deriving from it, helped us to understand the dynamics of this family and was useful in planning treatment strategy for them.

FAMILY ART EVALUATION WITH THE
VALACHOS FAMILY

A series of pictures by one family will illustrate the sequence of procedures in family art evaluation and the impact of one on the other. The total evaluation provides not only conventional diagnostic information but also a clear view of the family's relationships and focal conflicts. In the Valachos family, Evelyn, the recognized patient, was hospitalized at the Clinical Center of the National Institutes of Health. Her parents and siblings were seen as outpatients.*

Evelyn was eighteen-years-old, the oldest daughter in a middle-class family. About a year before her admission to the Clinical Center she had left college only three days after arriving there. She had had difficulty concentrating, was preoccupied with her obesity and with masturbation, and feared she might have a venereal disease. Later, after an unhappy affair, she became mute, negativistic and withdrawn, as well as transiently suicidal. Of her four siblings only the two older ones, Vicky, age sixteen, and George, age thirteen, were taking part in family psychotherapy, in research interviews, and in family art evaluation. Laughter was their constant defense. One sensed the patient's anxiety and discomfort, but the family brought enough humor into the evaluation session to make it relatively easy to bear.

Although five of the seven family members were present, I am going to concentrate on the three around whom the conflict seemed to focus: mother, father and Evelyn. I will discuss only the pictures most significant for the understanding of the family's dynamics.

Figure 48, "Our family," a family portrait drawn by Mrs. Valachos, is rather immature and could easily be attributed to a child between eight and ten years of age. There are no gross distortions except for the infantile appearance of all family members; mother hardly looks older than her five-year-old daughter. The father does not appear much more grown up but he leads the

---

*The material on this family was reported previously in Hanna Yaxa Kwiatkowska: The use of families' art productions for psychiatric evaluation. *Bulletin of Art Therapy*, 6(2):52-69, 1967.

group. The mother drew herself next to him, then crossed out
her name and placed the patient's name under the figure instead.

Figure 48.

Figures 49, 50 and 51 are abstract family portraits, drawn by
Evelyn, Vicky and George. Looking at Evelyn's drawing, Figure
49, we see that this girl's thinking is very concrete and that her
symbols are overgeneralized. Women in the family are flowers
and boys are toy animals; the father, however, is a big strong
tree. It is interesting that Evelyn at first refused to draw herself
in the family group. It was only when the session was over and
the family was ready to leave that she shyly asked, "May I add
something to one of my pictures?" She then drew one red flower
at the end of the row, wrote her mother's name under it, crossed
out the inscription "Mommy" from under the flower next to the
father and wrote her own name instead. She said she did not
want to be "left out."

These substitutions, indicating confusion of identity on the
part of both mother and daughter, were certainly not without

Figure 49.

meaning. Evelyn's and mother's roles were shifting: Evelyn displaced mother, mother displaced herself. Our first thought was that this might be an expression of the oedipal conflict. The later course of the session, however, indicated that the conflict might also be preoedipal, concerned with Evelyn's wish to take the mother's place in a nurturant role.

Figure 50 is an abstract family portrait made by Evelyn's sister Vicky. Vicky was less concrete than Evelyn; she used movement and color successfully to represent the different personalities. The ladder or vertical fence-like shape on the left is inscribed "Daddy—organized, sensible, stable." Next to him the wavy multicolored lines are "Mommy—bubbly, emotional, changeable." Evelyn is represented by a hand, inscribed "helpful, sensible." We are struck by the contrast between these adjectives and the character of the hand, which hangs like an empty rubber glove, lifeless and entirely devoid of the helpful strength it is supposed to have.

Figure 51 is George's abstract family portrait. He pictured

Daddy as a "Wise Owl," Mommy as a red mouth labeled "A Merry Smile," his sister, the patient, as a halo entitled "Good."

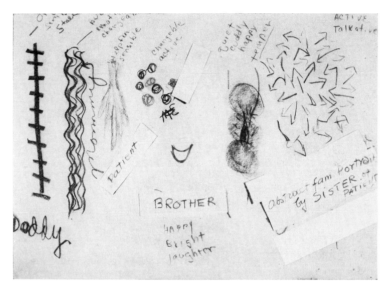

Figure 50.

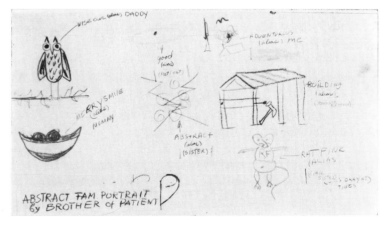

Figure 51.

We see a consistent image of the father, the mother and the patient in these three abstract family portraits:

1. The father is a pillar of strength and a source of wisdom (tree, ladder, owl).
2. The mother is the merry, changeable, unstable creature (red flower, bright wavy lines, smiling mouth).
3. The patient navigates between the parents in an indefinite role—competitive or complementary?

During the session George and Vicky were constantly teasing their mother about her foolishness, nuttiness, helplessness, and lack of talent. Actually she managed well and was able to carry out all required tasks.

We also notice that in their abstract family portraits the well siblings represented this trio, mother, father and patient, next to one another, while the patient and the mother shifted themselves from place to place in their own pictures.

Let us look now at Figures 52 and 53, individual pictures developed from scribbles by Evelyn and her sister. Figure 52 is by the patient. She chose just a fragment of the scribble and made no changes in its lines. The final result shows her inability to creatively integrate fragments into a whole (we saw a similar treatment of the scribble in Figure 23). Such coloring-in of shapes formed by the scribbled lines instead of using these forms as a stimulus for the imagination is characteristic of fragmented or constricted schizophrenics. I later found that she was indeed diagnosed as a constricted, schizoid personality with occasional circumscribed, frankly schizophrenic episodes. Evelyn's picture is not an extreme example, since she gave the colored portion of her lines meaning with the title "Goose Head" in an effort to achieve more than just a filling-in of space.

Figure 53, "Mating Season," is Vicky's drawing. Notice the difference between this and Figure 52 by Evelyn. The picture Vicky developed from her scribble displays her freedom and imagination. She departed from the original lines to develop her idea and then freely added other shapes and colors. She became involved in the creative activity and ended up with a delightful harmonious and complete picture. Her title, whatever its implications may be, is also imaginative and suggests a meaning far beyond the labeling of the obvious.

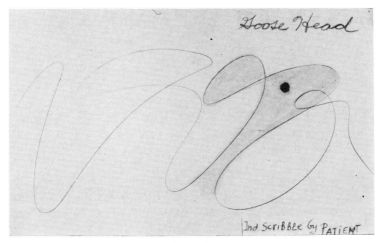

Figure 52.

Vicky, the well sibling, showed in all her individual pictures consistently good integration and ability for organized abstract thinking. So-called well siblings in many of the families with whom we work, however, demonstrate no such capacity. Fre-

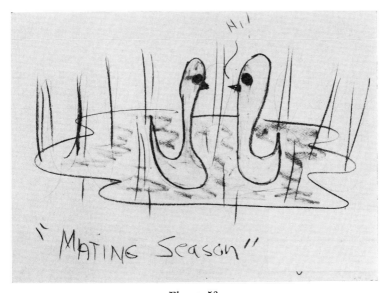

Figure 53.

quently we have noticed that a sibling whose behavioral and educational adjustment is adequate shows in his pictures signs of underlying thought disorder or personality problems.[16]

An example of the joint family scribble will help us to see how the Valachos family functioned in a joint enterprise.

It happens frequently that families, especially those with a schizophrenic member, decide which scribble to develop on the basis of who made it rather than because of what they see in it. Reasons for this vary. It may be in order to give support to the family member felt to be the weakest, or, on the contrary, to emphasize someone's role as the key figure in the family problems. We must realize that we are speaking here of the roles attributed by the family to its different members; these may be quite different from their actual roles in the family.

The Valachos family chose mother's scribble without even looking at the others. We remember the family's view of the mother as "merry, unstable, changeable," in contrast to the father as a "pillar of strength." It would appear that the family was focusing on the mother as a vulnerable person who needed support and attention. In later pictures and in the course of family therapy Mrs. Valachos proved to be much stronger and less vulnerable than her husband.

There were many different associations with mother's scribble, but finally Vicky forced the decision by simply asking whether everybody agreed to father's first idea, a man reading the Sunday News. They managed to produce a fairly complete picture (Fig. 54), but it is limited on the whole to the original lines of the scribble (Fig. 55) just like Evelyn's individual scribble picture (Fig. 52), even though I had repeated a couple of times my initial instruction, "You can add, omit or change as many lines of the scribble as you want." The phallic character of the newspaper is puzzling and adds a bizarre note to the otherwise humorous and imaginative, even if somewhat limited, picture. Evelyn's father and brother did most of the drawing.

Figure 54.

The family was fairly gifted artistically and one would have expected them to be able to change the shape of the newspaper to one more pleasing and realistic. But the father's constriction and rigidity, which we were better able to understand as the family art evaluation proceeded, did not allow him or the other family members to depart from the shapes that were there at the start.

We became especially aware of this characteristic when we later compared Mr. Valachos' free pictures made in the first and last procedures. Through this comparison we learned much about his ego strength and about how he had been affected by what appeared in the family's pictures. Mr. Valachos looked as if he were

Figure 55.

fairly well adjusted and, as we have noted, he was represented by his children as strong and wise. But was he as solid as he appeared?

Figure 56, "Quiet Country Scene," his first picture, was drawn with freedom and ease. Mrs. Valachos commented, "This is what he wishes for, a farm." Let us compare it with "Fields of Grain" (Fig. 57), his free picture produced at the end of the session.

We see a complete change from the pleasant, carefree "Quiet Country Scene" to these empty and forbidding rows of fences. In the light of this change one wonders how burdensome it was for him to maintain the role of "pillar of strength" assigned to him by his family. Was he able to live up to their expectations?

He might also have been responding defensively to the danger

Figure 56.

of the triangle: his wife, Evelyn and himself. We recall the earlier pictures (Figs. 48 and 49), in the first of which mother displaced herself next to him with Evelyn, and in the second of which Evelyn displaced her mother next to him with herself. How much was he threatened by the unclear, complicated aspects of this relationship? It appears that he had to protect himself by denying all feeling; he was expected to be as "wise as an owl" and "reliable, organized, sensible." In his last free picture he built fences and barriers around himself, while at the beginning of the session he was able to express a poetic fantasy, a cherished wish.

The family art evaluation with the Valachos family revealed

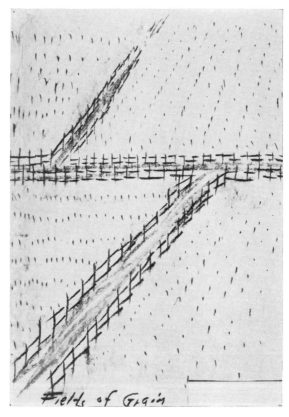

Figure 57.

facets of their personalities—their strengths, weaknesses and inter-relationships—that were very different from the stereotyped roles they assumed. In the single evaluative session these complicated and delicate aspects of the family dynamics were clearly displayed and were noted by the therapists. Caution had to be used, however, in calling the family's attention to these revelations at that period of treatment. Nonetheless, this valuable material was made available to the therapists and family for use in the further course of verbal family therapy. Its tangible, visual form made it difficult for the family to deny or to ignore the symbolic messages it contained.

CHAPTER VIII

THE USE OF SCULPTURE IN FAMILY ART THERAPY

IN THE CASES presented thus far no examples were given of families' sculptures. The greater availability of pictorial than sculptural material in the National Institute of Mental Health sample results mostly from inadequate facilities for the latter. Most of the family art therapy sessions were conducted in a regular interview room equipped with a one-way mirror for the observers and for videotaping. There were no available water and sink; tables or sculpture stands could not be fitted in the room. However, some families not regularly observed by other therapists and staff were seen in an art therapy room where work in clay was possible.

In family art evaluations, since the art medium, pastels, had to be uniform for all families, clay could not be used. Also, because many of the case examples presented in this book revolved around family art evaluations, graphic material predominates.

While reflecting on the paucity of sculptures in the material I had collected through the years, I considered the possibility that there might be a reason other than the practical one for this phenomenon. Being a professional sculptor and having taught sculpture for a good part of my life may have created for me certain problems in the therapeutic situation. Had I feared carrying over my role as a teacher and focusing too much on the quality of the product? Would it have been difficult not to interfere with the work and give too much technical advice, more sought generally in work with clay because of the inherent difficulties in handling it?

It is only in retrospect that these thoughts came to my mind. I share them with the reader in order to call the attention of artists/art therapists to the possible traps in the switch from one identity to another or in combining them without detriment to the therapeutic process.

Following are several examples of the use of sculpture in family art therapy.

Mr. Ross, father of Charles (who was a chronic schizophrenic nineteen-year-old patient) monopolized the family art therapy sessions with his angry speeches aimed at the whole world, disrupting any attempts at meaningful communication between other family members and the therapists.

Given the choice of medium, Mr. Ross usually preferred to work in clay. His sculptures usually combined his paranoid views of the world with aggressive and destructive drives. His sculptures varied from sexy female figures to heads of political leaders, all of the latter globally hated by him regardless of their political views.

He had a system of punching and pushing the clay in a destructive and aggressive manner tinged with sexuality. He produced a number of heads of political personalities, ranging from Napoleon through Churchill to Kennedy.

Figure 58 shows a bust on which he worked for four months. The bust represents the United States president then in office. Mr. Ross used a mallet to pound the clay, put matches in his nostrils, and asked for pins to stick into him, thus torturing the bust, but finally arrived at the disdainful conclusion that "he is not worth torturing."

For this man sculpture was an excellent outlet for his hostility. He used clay at the level of a young child. His hatred of the whole world climaxed in this bust. He could not separate from it. This direct expression of his overwhelming anger appeared to be of some comfort to him.

His son's paranoid fantasies, ranging from killing his roommates and parents to blasphemous thoughts, seemed to be a pro-

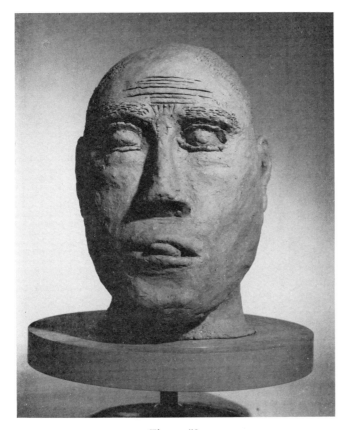

Figure 58.

jection of his father's paranoia. During the art therapy sessions Charles tried to join his father in his angry tirades but was usually rebuffed by him.

After four months of work on this bust, Mr. Ross seemed finally to have exhausted all the pleasure he could obtain from inflicting voodoo-like torture on the president. His last touch was to add a stuck-out tongue and the epithet "The Village Idiot."*

The therapeutic effect of this sculpture was mainly a cathartic

---

*The president depicted in this example is not identified for reason of confidentiality; the bust does not resemble him.

experience for Mr. Ross. However, it allowed the therapists to examine with the family their feelings in relation to the father's constant angry outbursts.

The next example (Fig. 59) is a sculpture fairly skillfully done by a fifty-six-year-old woman, mother of a twenty-seven-year-old schizophrenic. While working on it, she spoke of her wish that she had had a closer, playful relationship with her son when he was a baby. This is what she wished to portray. She accused her husband of not having let her show tenderness to their son lest she make of him "a sissy."

Figure 59.

Having completed her piece, she examined it carefully from all angles and became quite upset. She exclaimed that what really came out in the sculpture was a gesture of simultaneously holding the baby and pushing it away from her. In Figure 60 we see better the angle that was so upsetting to her. However, an objective viewer would not see so striking a gesture of rejection. Her interpretation of this sculpture seemed to be a projection of her true feelings toward her son: on the one hand, her inability to be close to him, and on the other, her inability to separate from him. We notice a fusion of both figures, which would confirm the symbiotic relationship from which she could not extricate herself.

Figure 60.

The sculpture and the mother's comments stimulated the parents to discuss their mutual accusations of having contributed to their son's illness. This provided ample therapeutic material that had been otherwise difficult to reach.

Another double message, but in a more bizarre form, is found in the two-faced head, one smiling and one angry or sad (Figs. 61 and 62). This strange sculpture was by Mr. Hall, a man in his fifties, father of a schizophrenic girl. Mr. Hall functioned quite adequately, was a good provider for his family, and had no known history of psychological disorders. But when left to use a regressive material, he freely expressed some bizarre fantasies. He never explained the beak on the side of the two-faced head (Fig. 63). Another head he modeled (Fig. 64) bears the same scarf knotted around its neck as does the two-faced head, giving a strangling effect.

Figure 61.

Figure 62.

Figure 63.

Figure 64.

His underlying psychopathology was not manifested in his behavior or his verbal communication. But as we saw in a number
of parents of schizophrenic patients, it became evident through a
more primitive, less controlled mode of expression.

CHAPTER IX

FAMILY ART THERAPY AS THE PRIMARY MODE OF TREATMENT

FAMILY ART THERAPY as the primary mode of treatment is certainly the most challenging and rewarding application of art techniques with families. However, it also demands a solid background in family therapy and extensive psychotherapeutic experience in addition to art therapy training.

This work, at least in my experience, is usually conducted in collaboration with a psychiatrist-cotherapist, and the responsibility for the treatment is entirely in the hands of the psychiatrist/ art therapist team. This responsibility is particularly serious when the patient is not hospitalized but is seen with the family on an outpatient basis. Outpatients and their families do not have the benefit of other therapeutic modalities available to varying degrees in a hospital treatment program, such as individual, couple, group and milieu therapies, along with therapeutic ward activities.

Here the total therapeutic endeavor is concentrated on the use of graphic media as the primary mode of communication and treatment. We have found that in this setting verbal exchange between therapists and family members has proved to be most therapeutically fruitful when it is stimulated by and directly connected with their art productions. The question arises, for what kind of families is this form of therapy indicated?

With many patients or families seeking help, traditional psychoanalytically oriented therapeutic methods have not proved to be outstandingly effective. Particular difficulties arise in therapy with families, one of whose members presents schizophrenic symptoms.* Younger children's participation in family therapy also presents problems in verbal communication. The unequal emotional and developmental levels of the family group may entail special difficulties for the therapist. He has to find a common starting point, a common denominator that will be equally accessible both to him and to each member of the family. The therapist may approach the family at a level above their reach; he may also be hampered by the family's unequal verbal skills. Expression through graphic media may help overcome these difficulties. It permits communication on a primitive level accessible to all family members, regardless of their ages or degree of illness. It is task oriented; its products are tangible and durable and can be reviewed. Therefore, it helps the family to focus on issues that would otherwise vanish before they can be explored.

Families of schizophrenic subjects also find it hard to share foci of attention;[22] many utterances are so vague and amorphous that after the words are said not much is left to reflect upon. There is no continuity from one session to another, so there is little possibility of returning to a problem touched upon at a previous session that needs to be further explored. When dealing with pictorial material, the concrete image serves as a connection between one session and another and helps to maintain some continuity of the therapeutic process.

We have found family art therapy also to be quite suitable for hysteric families with a tendency to act out their emotions. It seems that immature, infantile people respond better to a more primitive and action-oriented approach than to verbal exchange. (We saw an example of this in Chapter IV, where we described the course of therapy with a family with a hysteric daughter. Although in that case family art therapy was used as an adjunct and in parallel to verbal family therapy, the principles of their response is the same.)

Family art therapy as the primary mode of treatment has been

---

*Observations of art productions and of the process of creating them by families with a schizophrenic member have been touched upon in Chapter VI.

used at the National Institute of Mental Health in short-term treatment (three months) and in long-term treatment (up to one and one-half years). Of course, technique and therapeutic goals are determined to some extent by the length of treatment, as with any other therapeutic method.

Short-term family art therapy concentrates more on the solution of immediate problems. The problem, or what the family sees as a problem, is often represented spontaneously in their first pictures. However, as we saw in examples presented earlier, the focus often switches because of the way different family members present their views of the problem. The initial reason for seeking treatment is overshadowed by a totally different aspect of the family disturbance brought to their awareness through their art productions.

In Chapter VII we gave examples of the message of the first pictures (Figs. 32 and 33). We soon understood in that case that the underachievement of the identified patient resulted from the severe depression of the mother. The mother's problem came to the surface in these first pictures, and the role of the patient switched from daughter to mother.

In long-term family art therapy, therapeutic goals may emerge more gradually. However, we have found that even in the first session we also usually learn a great deal about family members' roles and relations.

As an example of long-term treatment, I shall describe briefly a year and a half of family art therapy with a family with a schizophrenic member.*

A staff psychiatrist's interest in the graphic technique was aroused by the rich material he discovered in an art evaluation when a family with whom he had worked for some time was about to be discharged. We therefore looked for a suitable family to treat in long-term family art therapy.

The family to be described was known to have changed therapies and therapists repeatedly and that it was again shopping for therapy. We were eager to start and the Wadners were available, so we embarked on this long joint venture. We began work-

*Dr. F. Gentry Harris is coauthor of the case description that follows.

ing with them as outpatients, with the sessions conducted by the initial psychiatrist and me as cotherapists, and later, upon his departure, by his successor and me. The successor psychiatrist observed through a one-way mirror and followed and discussed with us all sessions from the beginning.

We decided not to go through the traditional study of the family's history. We knew only that Donny, eighteen years old, had recently been a patient in a state hospital with a diagnosis of schizophrenia and was presently at home on some kind of probationary status. The reasons for the hospitalization were not initially clear to us and for a long time they were not disclosed by the family.

Such a procedure may surprise some of our readers and colleagues. We had medical records available, of course, and could always refer to them if need be. But this did not become necessary; we came to know the family first-hand with the help of their pictures.

At the end of treatment we studied all the available records and were glad we had not done so earlier. We felt that our gradual direct discovery of the family brought facts more clearly to light and led us to a deeper understanding of this family. It was better not to be encumbered by others' sometimes contradictory opinions.

Graphic media were used from the first contact on. An easel, 18 by 24-inch paper, a felt-tipped pen, and a set of square-edged pastels had been prepared for each family member. In general, specific tasks were not assigned, but the evaluative procedures were gradually introduced and periodically repeated. Another art medium, tempera paint, was later added.

Initial weekly one-hour sessions were expanded to one and one-half hours, since we found that additional time was needed for producing the pictures and discussing them adequately. In sessions in which the material that had come out in previous pictures had not been sufficiently explored, no pictures were drawn and the family was not urged to produce any. The production of new pictures at such times may serve as a maneuver to cut short discussion of charged or painful issues.

Following is a description of the family as we first saw them.

Mrs. Wadner, the mother, age thirty-nine, was plump, blond and rather attractive. A smile was constantly glued on her face. She was the spokesman for the family.

Mr. Wadner, the father, age forty-eight, was rather pleasant looking. His slightly watery eyes and something about his complexion made us suspect that he was an alcoholic. He was quiet and withdrawn and had little to say. Both mother and father were government employees; the family resided in the southeastern part of the District of Columbia.

Donny, the identified patient, was eighteen years old. He was attractive and seductively doe-eyed; his good looks were spoiled by irregular teeth and the expression of his mouth. He was emaciated and frail and had poor posture.

Billy, Donny's seventeen-year-old brother, was athletic and well-developed, the complete opposite of his brother. Also, he was less handsome but more masculine. He resembled the mother and smiled most of the time, as she did.

The family was quite ungifted for drawing and painting, with the exception of the father, who showed some natural skill.

Upon their arrival at the preadmission session, the Wadners were advised that expressive use of the art materials laid out would be the method of work. They accepted the idea better than we had expected. This confirmed our hope that the family might be less defensive when using a medium of communication not as direct as words. They willingly started to draw and presented themselves to the therapists in their pictures at the first session.

Donny's first picture (Fig. 65) was a large inscription in block letters, "HATE." The hate seems to be all-counsuming and undirected, with no relationship to anything or anyone.

Mr. Wadner drew a "Tank" (Fig. 66). This picture brought him to speak of his experiences during World War II; he had been a tank gunner and had been wounded while inside a tank by a "German version of the bazooka." He was awarded the Silver Star. He would have preferred to be a gunner in the Air Corps, though he had no interest in flying. He likes to shoot. Surprisingly, the family had never heard of his interest in shoot-

Figure 65.

ing. The mother said, with amazement, "He does not like to hunt; he does not own a gun." At this point the father observed, "A person might like to throw rocks, you know." This picture seemed to us to be a secret wish or view of himself, a part of what the family did not know about him—his hidden aggression. He later said about his war experiences, "The Army is the one place you can be what you want to be."

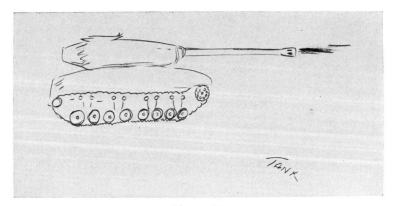

Figure 66.

The "Tree House" (Fig. 67), by Billy, was a place where he met with a group of his friends. He described and explained the tree house with great enthusiasm and involvement, almost euphoria, as if he wanted to include us in his secret world. We felt the healthy aspect of this picture to be its depiction of separation from the family, but with a definite objective and with other people. As we became aware later, an unhealthy aspect might be that the separation was premature. The drawing indicates the parental home in the distance, as if hung on a line, suggesting instability and lack of security. In this session Billy was more involved with us; maybe he had hopes for some kind of magic from us. Later in the treatment he became bitter and apathetic. The sexual symbol seen in some shapes in the picture suggest a possible sexual activity in the tree house. However, this may also be the first clue to the sexual stimulation within the family, of which we gradually learned.

Mother at the first session drew "Lassie" (Fig. 68), the family dog around which all the family's affection apparently centered. We saw this picture as mother's ambivalent expression of a wish to be the dog, the object of the family's affection, and at the same

Figure 67.

time as a complaint of being treated like a dog by the three males with whom she was constantly struggling. Later in the course of therapy other thoughts about the significance of the dog came to mind. The dog could be considered a transitional object,[23] comparable to the blanket carried by a child: a thing that both is and is not the object one is concerned with, half symbol and half object, and thereby satisfying and manageable. For the mother, who was living in constant struggle with the three males that was both defensive and devouring, the dog as a transitional object may have been the only living thing to which she could safely express open warmth and concern.

Figure 68.

At the next session the family was introduced to the use of a scribble as the starting point for a picture. During the first part of this session Donny remained silent, except for some occasional moan-like noises. But he came suddenly to life and went to his mother's scribble, turned it 90 degrees, and drew on it what he called "Side Rooms" (Fig. 69). This was his first effort toward finding meaning in a picture. He spoke of how he was "thrown" into the seclusion room of the hospital because "I was suspicious, [he corrected himself] no, suspected of doing something I did not do. . . . This is the way they do to people—throw you in and forget about you." Mother said she never saw these rooms, and Donny retorted, "You never looked." This picture, used as an expression of abandonment and rejection, was an introduction to a theme that came up repeatedly for months: his resentment and anger at his parents, who came to visit him each week in the state hospital. The accusations were mainly addressed to the mother. His particular entanglement with his mother first appeared clearly here: his choice of his mother's scribble and then his turning directly to her in the expression of his grievances. The latter was a monotonous repetition of the same words, "She would bring candy, and smile, always smile, and then leave."

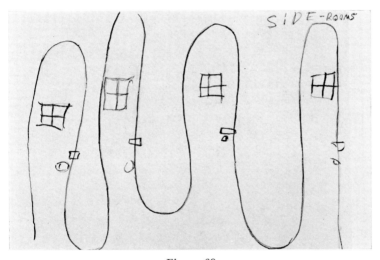

Figure 69.

In a later session we felt that it was time for the family to express in a more direct fashion their views of one another. We therefore suggested one of the evaluative procedures, an abstract family portrait. This technique is usually very revealing; with this family it was particularly impressive.

Donny's "abstract" representation of the family was concrete and extremely primitive (Fig. 70). It introduced the problem of the father's drinking (the bottle of "BUD"). Donny was bitter, contemptuous and accusing; he spoke with disgust of father's falling when drunk and his sleeping on the floor. Father said he drank "to escape a situation . . . anger, nerves. . . . There is no way to change the way *she* feels." Donny remarked about his drawing of mother, "Mother and her big mouth . . . never shuts up . . . and yells." Billy is represented as a football; two other shapes are crossed up and were not commented upon—Donny's uncertainty about his identity?

The title of Billy's abstract family portrait is "Terror & Devastation" (Fig. 71). He drew only the mother—a frightening whirlpool: "Mine is supposed to be like a hurricane. Mother always gets in the way and tells everyone what to do; she always gets her way." Mother denied any hostile meaning and with her eternal smile said, "It's cute." When Billy was asked by the father why he didn't draw the other family members, he answered, "I don't know why."

Figure 70.

In her abstract family portrait mother used color (Fig. 72). Billy, in blue, was explained as a "lazy slob"; the brown rectangle is herself: "I am fat and I like brown." Surprisingly to us and probably more so to the father, he is a sun. Donny is an addition: "4 plus 4 equals 8—because he is good in math."

In another abstract family portrait requested from the family seven months later, mother chose exactly the same mathematical form and the same numbers to represent herself, an interesting indication of her identification with Donny (Fig. 83).

Figure 71.

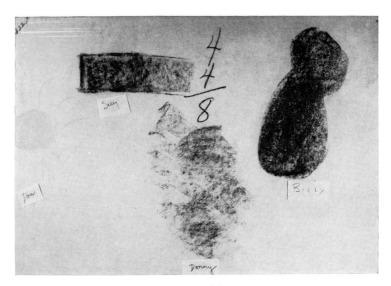

Figure 72.

Father's abstract family portrait (Fig. 73) carries a double message and is impressive by its inhuman quality. The whole family is represented as "machines." "Sally [the mother] and I produce" (but as we see, the output is nothing). The boys are two record players. There are locks on the record players, the father explained, "to keep them going." In reality these locks may be keeping them going, but only in circles, without a chance to get away from the family.

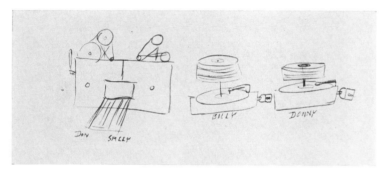

Figure 73.

Thus through the pictures we gradually learned more and more about the family. We could see the extremely passive father constantly nagged by the mother, who actually was as ineffective as he was. The mother explained one of her pictures, "House in Hartford" (not shown), as her own mother's house in Connecticut: "This is my real home; I even went there to give birth to both my children." We learned through this picture of her great dependency needs and her inability to detach herself from her mother. Later this was denied by her and she spoke differently of her relationship to her mother. She claimed that the parent to whom she had been really close was her father. Her use of the pictures thus gradually indicated that her own unresolved oedipal conflict was not without influence on the complicated current relations of the family.

In later pictures by the mother her preoccupation with Donny's physical care was shown (Fig. 74). Additionally, gestures

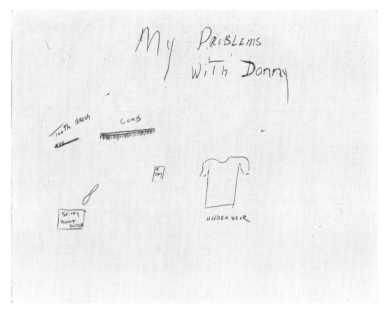

Figure 74.

observed during the sessions (like Billy's suddenly putting his leg on mother's lap) and mother's habit of running half dressed in the house, rather crudely reported by Donny, made us see more clearly the atmosphere of sexual excitation existing in the house. Billy's preoccupation with sex had originally been hinted at through the prominent phallic symbol in the "Tree House" (Fig. 67). Sexuality (pseudosexuality) was very diffuse in the family and consequently gave a sense of overwhelming complexity. Donny antagonized his peers at school by calling himself "a queer," but when confronted with the homosexual advances of a friend with whom he went on a vacation to Chicago, he panicked and spent a winter night in the streets of the city, afraid to return to the hotel room. The father had mentioned beforehand the possibility that this friend was a homosexual, but he passively allowed the trip and even drove them both to the train.

Donny at this point seemed to be in an undifferentiated stage of sexual development. He made seductive homosexual gestures, craved and cried for "caring" by his mother, got himself in trouble for peeping into women's windows, and made ineffectual propositions to girls very much his junior.

After we learned this much about the family, we felt that our next goal would be to find a leader for the family—a "President of the Family." At that time we still had hopes that the father, if adequately supported in this role, could carry it out. His artistic skill, better than the rest of the family's, could also be an asset in having him conduct the drawing and painting. Given this task in the third month of treatment, he seemed to enjoy the opportunity. His picture "Sunday" (Fig. 75), however, shows how he really perceived his and other typical roles in the family. He depicted his previous Sunday and explained that one of the boys is reading, the other is watching TV, mother is yelling, and he, having finished cleaning the stove, is taking care of the weekly wash!

Figure 75.

At the beginning of the treatment Donny presented himself as an indefinite, barely human, being. He uttered inarticulate

moans or repeated endlessly and irrelevantly his poorly formulated grievances and accusations against his parents and his
previous hospitalization (recall his first picture, "HATE," and his
other pictures done in the first weeks of treatment). With the
help of the pictures he was gradually able to achieve communication that went beyond a universal, undifferentiated hate or a
repetitious enumeration of complaints. We saw such communication introduced in symbolic fashion first in the picture he spontaneously painted and named "Family" (Fig. 76). The lines of
the picture strike us as strong and goal directed. He commented,
"You [father and mother] care for yourselves, I am alone, and
Billy is by himself. You [father] like mother no matter what she
does; you don't even stop her when she yells. Nobody cares what
happens to me as long as you both have nice private lives together
somewhere." We see here a clear and direct expression of his
competition with father for mother. But Donny gradually seems
also to be able to compete with father in a more constructive
manner.

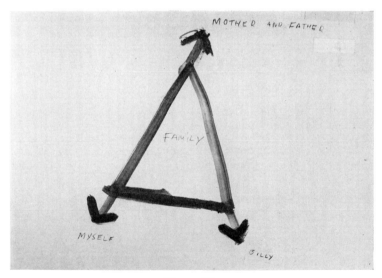

Figure 76.

A stormy period for the family followed. Donny found his
father lying drunk in the street; he rescued him and brought him

home. At the following therapy session Donny was the one to prod his father to take the lead. This was something new for Donny, who had up to now to be dragged into the activity. The father responded rather ineffectually. Finally, two weeks later, following a session the father had missed, Donny volunteered that maybe he could be what he called "the teacher." This was one of the turning points in therapy, as much from the point of view of the change in Donny's behavior as of the change in what he was able to represent pictorially.

When Donny acted as the leader, he suggested the subject "Three Wishes." He took his role as leader seriously and with authority. After the drawings were ready, he took charge of directing the discussion and showed much interest in the pictures of other family members. He explained his own picture, "Three Wishes" (Fig. 77), as follows: His first wish was for love, his second for money, and his third for happiness. Father drew only two wishes (Fig. 78). His first wish was for money, a diploma and car keys for Donny; and money, a diploma, a home and a wife for Billy. His second wish was that he and his wife be alone. He left a blank but numbered space for this third wish, though a

Figure 77.

third wish could have been attained by separating the wishes for each boy (thus note the failure to distinguish between the boys). Here we see father's wish for the sole possession of mother and exclusion of the boys lumped together, without any connection with her, a theme acknowledged earlier in Donny's picture "Family" (Fig. 76). Note also that Donny was the only one in the family to express a wish involving feelings.

Figure 78.

Both Billy and mother drew as their wishes unfulfillable fantasies: by Billy, of glory, "To put his mark on the world" (Fig. 79) ; and by mother, of escape into "Peace and Quiet" (Fig. 80). But Billy is also able to look more realistically at himself and his future. The tiny helpless figure we see on the left may well be the ambivalent wish to be on his own and the fear of independence, a subject that came out more directly at a later session. The second wish seems to be a rather healthy wish: money, a female companion, a house. But his third wish, and the only one he commented on, is an escape into a grandiose fantasy to leave a mark on the world—a pitiful wish by someone who at that time had so many needs and not much to offer. Mother's "Peace and Quiet"

(Fig. 80) is represented by a bed in which she can sleep late and quietly after the two boys leave the house (for the day or forever?). Her fantasy of traveling on a ship was later fulfilled. After termination of therapy the couple did travel extensively. But where is her husband in her wishes? We just see clouds in the sky; is he the cloud in her life?

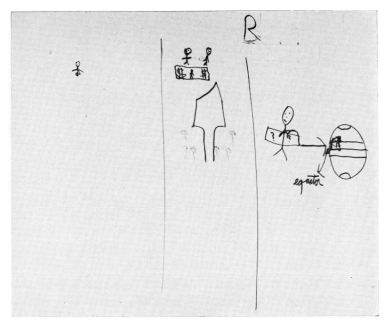

Figure 79.

Despite the visible change in Donny, we realized that the problems of the family were too deeply rooted not to expect periods of regression and of violent crises. The conflict the family had in dealing with feelings and the threat they presented to them was climaxed at the next session. The family was very tense. The mother prodded Donny by saying she was waiting for him to start the session. But being pushed by his mother may have been unbearable to Donny. He gradually worked himself into a complete loss of control. He started by reciting again and again his old accusations of his parents' neglect of him at the hospital. He

Figure 80.

started to scream, cry, drool and stomp his feet. He stood in front of his mother and dramatically shouted at her, "Did you care, did you care? Were you sad?" The mother sat smiling and silent. The father attempted to answer for her, and between Donny's screams he tried to describe mother's sleepless nights of worry. Finally mother stood up, crying and screaming, "I cannot stand it anymore!" and ran out of the room.

A point to note here is the terrible threat that the acknowledgment of her feelings of caring for Donny presented to this mother. It was at the moment when father disclosed them that she broke down and left.

Following this there was evidence that the family had doubts about their continued acceptability to us. The onus was placed on Donny, however, primarily through their revealing Donny's legal probationary status as a "peeping Tom" that, as we eventually learned, was the original reason for his hospitalization. Donny had simply denied his voyeuristic tendencies until the details were carefully extracted and put together in a form that made sense, whereupon he admitted his sexual curiosity and his ill-executed exploratory attempts to satisfy it.

In the sixth month of treatment no pictures were made. So much had been stirred up that we felt stimulation into expressive activity was contraindicated. New production of pictures could be used by the family defensively. We therefore concentrated on deeper verbal exploration of material projected in the last series of pictures.

The father's fading leadership died quietly two weeks later, when he came in quite sick with the flu and "did not feel up to taking over." No one spoke of it later; we felt that he was incapable of leadership even if it were given to him.

The interim was taken up with a good deal of attention to Billy, his plans upon graduation, and his possible draft into the Army. Billy was defiant and unrealistic about these plans.

During the seventh month we repeated some of the evaluation procedures. It can be seen from the following pictures what changes had occurred in the family's perception of themselves and of each other.

In Donny's second abstract family portrait, "Family Hate" (Fig. 81), the "hate" is still there, but it is small and on the side; it is no longer global and all-consuming. "They all hate, especially Mother." His father and Billy are included in the hate. He drew himself separate from them, however, quite large, with another female figure, identified by him only as "she." This could be seen as another projection of his wish to be in sole possession of the mother. In view of Donny's gradually emerging identity, it could also be a fantasy of a heterosexual relationship.

Billy's second abstract family portrait, "Year of the Lord" (Fig. 82), included this time three members of the family, not just the overwhelming mother of "Terror and Devastation" in his first family portrait (Fig. 71). However, he omitted himself from the picture. This appeared to be a more direct indication of his effort to separate himself from the family. The mother is the "lightning"; Donny is a gray nothingness; the father, again to our surprise, is a shining sun (note that mother also represented him thus in Figure 72).

Mother titled her second abstract family portrait "Family

Figure 81.

United" (Fig. 83). Billy and father are both present and absent; mother explains, "Don is in a cloud; Billy is sleeping. . . . Donny is trying to get over the barrier." One fascinating thing is that she now uses for herself the same mathematical form, "4 plus 4 equals 8," with which she had designed Donny in her first abstract family portrait, commenting now, "I am the only one who keeps order." This time her husband is no more the shining sun of her first abstract family portrait; a cloud covers it. We were so fascinated by her identification with Donny that somehow this was not adequately explored.

In his abstract family portrait, "Family" (Fig. 84), the father described his wife as "halo and horns . . . smiling now and frowning now . . . sometimes one and sometimes another; to the left we have me, who eventually gets all the crap in the family [but the crap is gloriously shiny!]. . . . Billy I portrayed as a bird . . . just a bird. . . . Donny a fish with teeth [the expression is characteistic for Donny's mouth]. A fish that does not care about others can sometimes be dangerous, not especially useful, because you can't eat it; you can't make a pet or a friend of it." Billy's representa-

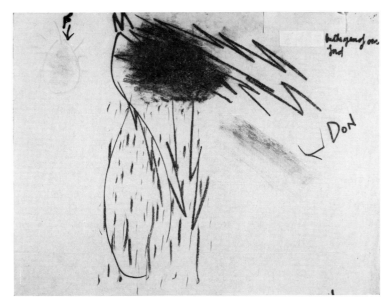

Figure 82.

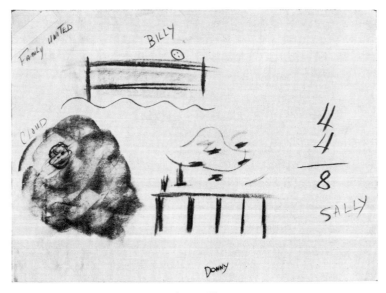

Figure 83.

tion as a bird is without doubt related to Billy's plans and desire to "fly away" from the family ties. Father's comments on the fish (Donny) are an expression of his contempt of Donny and his hopelessness in regard to this son.

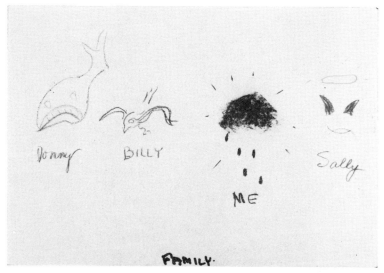

Figure 84

At the same session the family repeated another of the evaluative procedures: individual and joint pictures started by a scribble. Donny's picture "Paramecium" (misspelled "Paramiacium") (Fig. 85) started in this way. It is interesting because of the change in the investment, style and freedom with which he drew it, his associations, and his vivid explanations of "asexual division." Here we have a much clearer expression of the diffused and indefinite nature of Donny's problems with sexuality, which he brought up through free association and with a good deal of interest and appeal. Such determinate picturing of an indeterminate state of affairs could hardly be expected in the verbal medium. It may be surmised that this mode of communicating his current position with respect to sexual development afforded considerable relief and satisfaction, as well as a point of departure for further development.

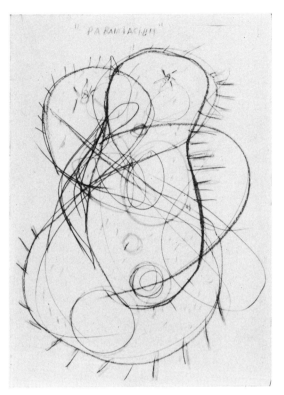

Figure 85.

"The Train" (Fig. 86) is a picture done jointly by the family. Each family member was asked to do his own scribble; they were then to decide jointly as a family which one they would agree to develop into a picture and draw the picture together. After these preliminaries the father quietly and unobtrusively took the lead and directed the construction of the picture. It was only in retrospect that we became aware of his leadership. The father was here given an opportunity to exercise his control and leadership in a more focused and limited situation, without its having to be openly acknowledged as such. He was better able this time and under these circumstances to lend a direction and organization to the efforts of the family not previously seen in the sessions. His fears of being attacked, and perhaps destroyed, seemed to have been lessened.

Figure 86.

In the spring both boys graduated from high school, which was problematic, especially for Billy. They both managed to get summer jobs, and for the first time in their lives were able to stay employed.

In the summer the psychiatrist-cotherapist advised the family that he would be leaving. The family showed no reaction during the first two sessions following this announcement, with the exception of Donny, who switched from his still frequent monotonous, repetitive accusations against his parents to an attempt to communicate through a picture how he felt about his psychiatrist's leaving.

In his picture "Careness—Isolation—SEE YOU NEXT WEEK" (Fig. 87) Donny crossed out the word "Careness." Donny seemed to be as fearful of feelings as was his mother. Characteristic for schizophrenic subjects is the fear of feeling. Feeling is connected with pain; therefore, as a defense against suffering it has to be denied, to cease to exist. Otherwise the picture seems to be an unusually clear expression of transference. Donny said about it, "You can read it." He added that his parents would come to see him in the hospital (where he had been behind bars), bring him candy, etc., and then leave, saying, "See you next week." It is noteworthy that for the title of his picture he used these same words, common at the end of a therapy hour, thus acknowledging his feeling of being abandoned by his psychiatrist as similar to what he had experienced so often in relation to his parents. Was he afraid of returning behind bars after the psychiatrist left? From then on he was able to verbally express sincere and direct grief. He also showed interest in the continuity of the treatment.

Figure 87.

At the last session before the departure of the psychiatrist, the other psychiatrist, who had observed all the sessions and who was to take over, was also present. The family was particularly listless and apathetic. It seemed that at this moment pictures might be helpful to the family in focusing more clearly on some of their feelings. It was therefore suggested that they draw whatever came to their minds.

Billy's "Dynasty of Doctors" (Fig. 88) seemed to express the feelings of the whole family. It was explained by Billy as follows: a golden pyramid in the background with one man (the departing psychiatrist) reading a scroll, the Ten Commandments, to another man (the new psychiatrist). The man being read to is represented as wondering how he is going to use the Commandments and is apprehensive about taking over. The therapists interpreted the four heavy blocks on a cart to the family as symbolic of the four family members, the idea being that Billy felt working with the family was equal to the task of building a pyramid, and a question whether the new psychiatrist would really be able to take the load.

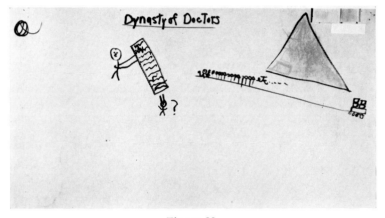

Figure 88.

Father's "Our Psychiatrist Goes West" (Fig. 89) shows a rider on a horse and four people in the background waving good-bye but looking away from the horseman. The family made some comments about how every person in the picture looks away from every other person. But we also notice that they turn away from the doctor who leaves turning his back on them. The picture can be seen as a reproach or retaliation: "If you don't care about us, we don't care about you." The sadness at the separation is denied. However, the family focusing on each person turning away from the other carries a note of their anxiety at how they will relate to each other when the psychiatrist will be gone.

Figure 89.

Donny arrived late and did not draw. He looked at his father's picture and said simply, "I wish I could go West." From then on, the problem that separation presented for the family was openly discussed. It also allowed an acknowledgment of Donny's chronic and ambivalent conflict about separation from his family, thus extending the significance of the psychiatrist's leaving. The separation was particularly deeply felt by this family because one of their central problems was the issue of being together but being distant from each other.

After the first psychiatrist left, Donny took up his original role of acting out the family's feelings. He again attacked his parents at home and in the therapy sessions and put irrational demands upon them. The family would conveniently focus on Donny's acting out as a way of denying their own feelings of rejection and anger. They, especially the mother, affirmed that they took the separation and the changes in stride. Despite that posture, the mother finally allowed herself to cry on several occasions without shame and without having to run away. It was nevertheless, only through the pictures they subsequently drew that some of their feelings came through more clearly and could be acknowledged, aided by recognizable pictorial form.

The first picture drawn by Donny in the presence of the new psychiatrist was again called "HATE!" (Fig. 90), as had been his first self-introduction at the beginning of therapy (Fig. 65). We see a dismayed solitary figure of himself, his mouth distorted by a grimace. We remarked that he now drew himself alone, while not long before he had represented himself with a girl. We wondered if he felt lonesome, and Donny responded in a low voice that maybe this was so. This time the feeling was connected more with a personal experience rather than a global, undirected, all-consuming hate as in Figure 65.

Figure 90.

Father's picture, "Funeral" (Fig. 91), is particularly expressive. The seven people represented here fitted astonishingly well with the number of people involved in the therapy situation: the therapist who had left, perhaps dead in a casket, with the two other therapists and the family around him; only two of the faces are not grinning broadly—a male with glasses (the new psychiatrist) and a female with a hairdo somewhat similar to mine. It was seen differently by the mother. Before father had a chance to say anything about his picture, mother asked, pointing at one of the smiling faces, "Oh, I am laughing?" and "Why did you put yourself in a casket?" The father promptly explained the picture as the death of one of his neighbors. Interpretations relating this picture to the loss of the psychiatrist who had left were denied by the family. Interesting was the mother's comment; possibly she identified the departed psychiatrist with her husband, both of whom, she felt, had disappointed her.

FUNERAL

Figure 91.

Despite all the verbal denial, the therapists were able, with the help of the pictures, to point out to the family that there was more going on in their feelings and actions related to separation than they had been able to acknowledge or articulate.

Three sessions with the family were held jointly by the new psychiatrist and me before I left to be away for two months. Sessions with the whole family were discontinued for that period, but the new psychiatrist continued to work with the parents in the interim. The graphic medium was not used during that period.

In the fall work was resumed with the entire family and continued for four more months. During this period Donny's presence was sporadic; actually he appeared only at three sessions: the first time we all met together, then the week before Christmas —"A Christmas Present," as he called it—and at the termination session. At the first of these meetings Donny indicated his intention not to continue therapy, complaining that it was his parents, not he, who needed help and that he had decided to go his own way.

While Donny was the one who explicitly expressed his intention to separate himself from the therapy, the theme of aloofness and withdrawal appeared in all the pictures of this period. This aspect was particularly revealed in the following series of pictures.

After he drew a picture he called "SPECTATOR" (Fig. 92), the father spoke of his being a rather complacent outsider in the group as he watched the sessions from a distance. The picture gave the therapists material to bring to the family's awareness the extent to which Donny, in his wish to discontinue family therapy, was expressing something for other family members as well. This picture also prompted both brothers to talk of their wish that the father be less withdrawn and more assertive with the family.

Figure 92.

After this Donny stopped coming to the sessions altogether, and we met only with the parents and Billy. The mother increasingly took a background position and occasionally missed sessions. However, she was able, without interfering, to let the father and Billy engage in discussions and disagreements to an extent not previously seen.

An issue during this time was the continued remoteness of the father, with a good deal of the therapists' efforts directed toward more engagement with him. These efforts to prod the father into a more active and useful participation prompted him to produce a striking picture, "Good King Don" (Fig. 93). We see here a powerful and grandiose representation of himself with a much more open expression of his underlying murderous rage. It was in connection with this picture that the father eventually was able to talk of his reluctance to set limits on his sons for fear of losing control of himself to the point of violent action. We remember his first picture, the "Tank" (Fig. 66); his present comments revealed his aggression, usually concealed under a mask of passivity.

Figure 93.

The original plan was that therapy be continued for six more months, when the new psychiatrist would leave the National Institute of Mental Health for another position. By midwinter several missed appointments by mother and the continued absence of Donny led us to emphasize that for art therapy to be of use to the family all the family members had to be present. The family, with its markedly ambivalent feelings about continuing, un-doubtedly connected with their feelings of abandonment by the first psychiatrist, did little to deal with Donny about his coming to the sessions. In view of this difficulty, we set a termination date a month later. The family's reaction was comfortably focused on Donny's absence. As had been the case early in therapy, Donny seemed to be the messenger for the other family members.

During the period of therapy when Donny was absent, Billy took advantage of his absence and monopolized the role of the primary patient, thus availing himself of the greater opportunity to discuss his problems, which seemed to have become quite press-ing at this time. He dropped out of junior college, was unable to find a job, and had serious arguments with his father as a conse-quence of his impulsive and immature actions. Eventually the father threatened to throw him out of the home. At a subsequent therapy session he unexpectedly announced to the parents his decision to join the Army. It was at this time that he drew the picture "On the Outside Lookin' In" (Fig. 94), through which he became aware of his ambivalence about leaving. He explained the picture: He is standing on the outside of the home with a telescope and looking inside, where his parents are comfortably settled around the fireplace and financially secure, as indicated by the dollar symbol (figures in the top part of the house). We see on the right, however, a large figure with two small ones next to it. He identified these as his mother, Donny and himself. It was only later, when the therapists called his attention to it, that he realized he had drawn himself both inside and outside the house and was thus able to recognize his real desire to stay under the protection of the powerful mother. In this case it would be most improbable that a medium of communication other than drawing could apprehend so clearly and deal with such ambivalence.

Figure 94.

On termination day all the family members came. Each of their spontaneously drawn pictures was related to their feelings of insecurity and was in a way taking stock of the situation. Mother's picture "Cloud" (Fig. 95) made her reflect, "Where do we go from here?" Father gave as the title of his picture the date of the last session (Fig. 96). He was not asked to draw a family portrait, but did this picture spontaneously and said, "I still drink [the first time he admitted this directly]; my wife and Donny shoot the arrows at everyone else and at random. Donny is shooting a few arrows at you [the psychiatrist] and Mrs. K., which accounts for the other two there. I see Billy as a happy person; possibly that's the way I would want him to be." Note the arrows in this picture, similar to those in his earlier picture. "GOOD KING DON" (Fig. 93); they reinforce our impression that he saw his wife and Donny as the attackers. He contained his violent feelings of retaliation by grandiose aloofness or by drinking.

Donny's picture, "MY FUTURE?" (Fig. 97), was perhaps the

most expressive. He represented himself on a crossroad. He explained, "There's sort of a question mark there—uh—I had a miserable past and I guess the present is a little better than the past, but it should be better, I guess. . . . I don't know, it's. . . . I always end up somewhere . . . fog. . . . I could always—find a happy life—can always find a sad life as I could always." We see that his

Figure 95.

Figure 96.

use of words is strikingly inferior to the expressiveness of his graphic image. The poignant figure on the crossroads conveys a more defined, stronger message than the fussiness of his words. The smile suggests some hope for the future; perhaps therapy had allowed him to look at his future other than through the despair of his past.

Figure 97.

The family was then asked to make another abstract family portrait, the third in the series of such portraits done in the one and one-half years of treatment. Both Donny's and father's pictures were particularly eloquent. What Donny drew (Fig. 98) resembled his earlier picture of the paramecium (Fig. 85). Again his verbal utterance was blurred, one idea overlapping another, but finally, thanks to the concrete image, he could tell us that he felt isolated (we see him on the extreme right, "ME"), "and that's a problem by itself in getting, getting together when you are . . . isolated. I mean I'm more away from the family than I've been, than any other member of my family." He tried to explain what for a long time had been a very poor formulation of his ambivalence and therefore not clearly apprehended or communicable: He wants to detach himself from the family, but then he is isolated, "and this is a problem." We, and so does he, see the situation much more clearly in the picture: He is practically out of it, but still attached to his formidable mother, while his father and brother are tiny figures lost in the background. Would he ever have been able to communicate and realize through his foggy verbal statements the intensity of his ambivalence, which is so clearly depicted in his drawing?

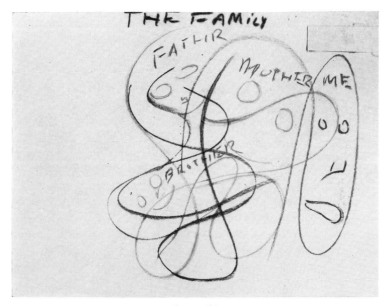

Figure 98.

The father explained his picture, also an abstract family portrait (Fig. 99):

I drew my wife as a lovable valentine — with thorns — you can look at her, but you can't get too close, because you may get stuck. And Donny is also something that you would like to sympathize with or like to get closer to, but feel so — as his thorns or arrows or spikes — and Billy I figured as something like the sun, or fire, warmth. And I am a bird — just an old bird.

Figure 99.

In Figure 84, his second abstract family portrait, note that he had represented Billy as a bird. Note also that the father now differentiates his sons as having more distinct personalities and as being more alive, while in Figure 73, his first family portrait, he had lumped them as identical locked machines. This picture repeats his perceptions of his wife and sons that we observed in earlier pictures. Both he and Billy seek escape (in flying away, or drinking) from the family problems. However, he now sees some positive qualities in his wife and Donny, possibly recognized in the course of therapy. But both are unpredictable and attack when attempts at closeness are made.

The work with the family often seemed arid and unrewarding, the psychopathology at times overwhelming. Yet as we reviewed the pictures we could see that out of this undifferentiated mass of pain, resentment and anger, more focused issues of their relationships with one another emerged and could be dealt with. At a session toward the end Donny said with astonishing clarity that their family was not a close one, but he felt that the closest relationships the family had ever had was during the time they had been coming here. His parting comments at the termination session attested to the usefulness of the graphic method. He saw "this . . . this art therapy" as "helping my thinking and getting my feelings out," an impressive statement when compared to his overwhelming "HATE" of eighteen months earlier. At the same session Billy expressed with visible emotion his heightened awareness that beneath the mother's constant nagging there was also concern for their well-being.

Both Donny and Billy demonstrated an increased competence in their planning and capacity to carry it through: Donny's work and preparation to attend college, and Billy's entrance into the Army.

The parents were better able to acknowledge their own problems, which had been worked on intensively during the period of therapy with the couple alone. They recognized gradually, even if often with a good dose of hostility, their mutual dependency on each other: the mother for the father's quiet control during her excited periods of upset, and he for his wife's capacity to manage family affairs when this seemed quite beyond him. The positive aspects of the mother's view of her husband began to emerge and perhaps shed some additional light on her original abstract family portrait in which she represented him as a "sun." The mother also seemed to have less need to hang on to her sons, and the boys were both able to relate to and identify more with a stronger side of their father, his reputable and gratifying army career. Both boys had also achieved a significant degree of autonomy on the long road to independence.

CHAPTER X

FAMILY ART TECHNIQUES AS RESEARCH TOOLS

B EFORE DESCRIBING the use of family art productions in research, it is necessary to consider the state of research in art therapy.

In the last decade the field of art therapy has made rapid progress toward professionalization. The infant, nebulous and ill-defined art therapy has finally gained recognition and respect. A national organization, the American Art Therapy Association (AATA), was founded in 1969. A number of universities have master's degree programs in art therapy and offer numerous undergraduate courses as well. In-service training in some hospitals and other institutions is also available.* Similar developments are taking place abroad.

Concomitantly, many art therapists have become increasingly interested in research. However, the profession is still struggling to find methods unique to the discipline.

In the basic principles of research, two approaches can be distinguished: systematic observation, without statistical analysis, of clinical procedures; and systematic examination of complex statistical analysis of empirical data. Both types of research are valid. The first is clinical and impressionistic, but clinical judgment can be collected and organized systematically and can offer solid conclusions if observations are carefully made and recorded. How-

---

*See Appendix II, a listing of educational opportunities in Art Therapy in the U.S.A., prepared by the Educational Committee of the American Art Therapy Association.

ever, one should be cautious about making generalizations that extend beyond the observed sample.

SYSTEMATIC NONSTATISTICAL RESEARCH

I will first present an example of research based not on statistical analysis but on clinical judgment stemming from systematically organized material.

In our project nine eminent mental health professionals—psychiatrists, psychoanalysts and psychologists—were asked to blindly study a series of pictures drawn during the course of long-term family art therapy as the primary mode of treatment.* We provided them with basic information about the family and with chronologically organized samples of their pictorial production.

For this 'project we used slides of pictures by the Wadner family, whose case was described in Chapter IX. We selected thirty-one pictures that we felt were the most revealing of the family's problems and relationships and provided the following basic data about the family:

1. Composition of family, with ages and sex of children.
2. Socioeconomic position.
3. Educational level of each family member.
4. Religion.
5. Information about the context in which the pictures were drawn: family art therapy as the primary mode of treatment; instruction, if any, given to the family at the time the pictures were drawn; titles and dates of pictures; special events during the course of therapy, such as changes or absences of therapists, or interruption or termination of therapy.

The identity and diagnosis of the family member who presented the symptoms that brought the family into treatment were not disclosed. No verbal comments by the family or therapists

---

*Dr. F. Gentry Harris[24] was my collaborator in this project. We are indebted to Drs. Robert Bagwell, Stephen Cohen, Allen T. Dittmann, William L. Granatir, John S. Kafka, Robert Kaye, Neda Maletic, Gary Morris and Jay T. Shurley for their most illuminating comments and impressively accurate conclusions.

were available to the judges.

The judges were asked to examine the slides of the pictures and respond to the following questions:

1. What do you feel you can say about any person from his pictures and what if anything about the family relationships?

2. What might be the therapy issues as reflected in the pictures?

3. Do you see any cues with regard to future therapy issues, problem areas, outcome, etc.?

We were also interested in comparing the judges' impressions with those of the family therapists and with the family members' own interpretations of their pictures.

In selecting the judges, we were primarily guided by their interest or experience either in art therapy techniques or in art generally. Of the nine judges who agreed to participate in our study, one had had a patient in long-term art therapy with me as an adjunct to the psychotherapeutic treatment of one of his patients. Several had observed families in art therapy or evaluation at the National Institute of Mental Health. None of the latter group had ever been a cotherapist in these modalities or had observed sessions with the Wadner family. All but one were interested in being "unblinded"; after the procedure was over, that one and two others expressed relief that they were through with their task; nevertheless, their evaluations were particularly perceptive. Only one of the judges did not indicate correctly the identified patient, but all diagnosed the family correctly as one with a schizophrenic offspring. The length of the judges' reports varied from three to twenty-eight pages.

In view of the limited number of judges and because only one sample was submitted to such a study, statistical analysis was out of the question. The judgments were nonetheless astonishingly accurate in their description of personalities, of the family relations and problems, and of the course and outcome of therapy.

Out of this wealth of material provided by the judges, while commenting on the whole set of thirty-one pictures, I have selected as examples pictures most often referred to by the judges or best illustrating the judges' inferences and conclusions.

Several of the judges noticed that in the series of pictures they looked at, there were more pictures by Donny than by the other members of the family and said this helped them to identify him as the patient. This may have been a flaw in our choice of pictures, but our choice was, in fact, guided only by how expressive the pictures were. Thus one can conclude that the schizophrenic patient is not only the family member on which the family focuses as "the problem" and the one maybe most burdened with the family conflicts, but is indeed also the one who carries the message.

Upon examining Donny's abstract family portrait (Figure 70, "Mother and her big mouth . . . never shuts up . . . and yells"), one of the judges, to whom, of course, Donny's comments were not available, remarked, "She could be helplessly dependent, verbally abusive, or devouring, demanding and overprotective." There could not have been a more accurate description of this mother.

The father, symbolized by Donny in the same picture (Fig. 70) by a bottle of "BUD" (beer), was thus described by one of the evaluators: "He retreated from his wife's anger and his own by absenting himself and drinking." We remember the father's response to Donny's representing him as "BUD." He had said he drank "to escape a situation . . . anger, nerves. . . . There is no way to change the way *she* feels."

Figure 69, "Side Rooms," by Donny (developed from his mother's scribble), was particularly perceptively commented upon by the judges. Three of them described this picture as suggesting prison windows. Another said, "He finds meaning in his mother's boring scribble. . . . The doors are closed, but at least there is a possibility of opening them [door knobs strongly outlined]. . . . Donny may be actually very accessible and the therapists might do well to try and draw him out."

Another judge observed, "Donny immediately identifies himself as the patient. He succeeds in indicating that a major axis in the family is the 'mother-Donny axis.' " As we remember from Chapter IX, Donny had explained this picture as the seclusion rooms in the State hospital he had been confined in. Turning to his mother, he had continued, "She would come, bring candy, and smile, always smile, and then leave." By choosing his mother's scribble and addressing to her his grievances about having been "thrown" in there and forgotten, Donny had given us evidence of his entanglement with his mother.

Mother's picture "Lassie" (Fig. 68) brought the following comment by one of the judges: "This mother can relate better to small children and animals than to adults." Closeness had been particularly threatening to the Wadner family, perhaps to the mother most of all. In Chapter IX we described how she broke down and left the session after Mr. Wadner disclosed her sleepless nights of worry when Donny was hospitalized. The dog she drew, as the judge was inclined to think, might have been the only living being to which she could relate with open warmth and affection.

Another judge commented about the same picture, "The drawing is cute, noncommittal . . . she may be an evasive woman unwilling to open up in therapy and very protective of herself and her defenses," which was another accurate definition of the way she had shown herself to be in therapy.

Billy had commented on his picture "Terror and Devastation" (Fig. 71), "Mine is supposed to be like a hurricane—Mother always . . . gets her way." One of the judges had the following interpretation: "Billy sees the family as a hopeless, confusing whirlwind . . . no boundaries for identifying objects . . . disintegration of the original scene. Is this boy a schizophrenic?" Another judge observed, "Everyone is caught up in intertwining circles, undifferentiated, unable to separate from each other, caught in a whirlpool and maze of depression, confusion and terror."

Aggressive impulses and the fear of not being able to control them was another characteristic of this family that came up in therapy and was particularly expressive in the father's pictures. The judges picked this up from Mr. Wadner's first picture, "Tank" (Fig. 66). One of the judges said, "Father . . . has hostility, but it is camouflaged by portraying weapons—'It is not I who destroy, it is my gun.'" Another judge said, "I think there is a great potential for anger . . . but . . . it appears in such disguised form." If we recall a picture by Mr. Wadner drawn later in the course of therapy, "Good King Don" (Fig. 93), we have confirmation of the accuracy of the judges' perception of him.

A further magnificently exact definition by the judges of this father's personality was based on his picture "Sunday" (Fig. 75). One of the judges commented, "Father is the most aloof from the rest of the family, off in the basement, doing the laundry. His shirt is colored red, but he does not express his anger or discontent—he passively submits . . . and I suppose gets drunk later."

Another comment on the same picture by one of the other judges: "Father is an isolated, chronically depressed man. Knows very little how to handle either anger or feelings of closeness and affection in spite of a relatively well-developed ego structure."

As we see, the judges, just from examining the series of pictures, caught what we were gradually made aware of in therapy. In the first months of treatment we saw the father as remote and ineffective, as if paralyzed by the overwhelming aggression hidden under his passivity. Eventually, with the help of the pictures, he was able to talk of his reluctance to set limits on his sons for fear of losing control to the point of violence.

"The Train" (Fig. 86), the joint picture started with the help of a scribble, was seen by one of the judges as "very imaginative . . . here there is something emerging, maybe a turning point in therapy." Another judge thus described both father and mother in connection with this endeavor: "The family was able to function very well in the joint scribble. My fantasy is that it is largely influenced by the father [it was] . . . filled with the drawing characteristics of father. Mother's chaos and smoke and diffusiveness goes right through the center of the train and then fills up the rest of the drawing, so mother's presence is everywhere as an amorphous non-nurturant tunnel."

An interesting aspect of this study is that though most of the pictures were very crude, some of the judges appreciated the aesthetic quality of a few of them. This improvement in quality corresponded to periods of progress in the course of therapy. In Chapter IX we called the attention of the reader to the change in the investment, style and freedom in the picture by Donny of a paramecium (Fig. 85). Through this picture he was able to bring out the diffused and indefinite nature of his sexual identity.

One of the judges commented, "Of all the drawings done by anyone in the family this one is by far the most lovely and aesthetic," but he also called attention to its "lack of organization."

Another judge stated, "In his protozoal form of life is concealed his longing for tenderness, for entwining himself in the arms of his mother . . . dependency and his expectation of love are too fraught with danger and thorns to trust himself or the situation sufficiently to picture this very clearly."

A reversal in Donny's style was noticed by the judges in a later picture drawn at the time the first psychiatrist was leaving, "Careness—Isolation—See you next week" (Fig. 87). One of the judges focused on the regressive quality of this drawing, a return to his earlier style after the flourishing period during which he had drawn the paramecium. Another observed, "Donny feels imprisoned when his psychiatrist leaves. He sees his salvation going away. Now he'll go crazy and get locked up." A third judge commented, "Donny experiences separation as an isolation or as a punishment."

We feel that the most impressive findings of this study were the thoughts of the judges about the outcome of therapy. They were mostly positive but cautious. I quote some of them:

> "I expect that there will be some stormy periods ahead yet for all concerned . . . but primarily I think of the likelihood of reestablishment of equilibrium in which the defensive structure of father and mother are not quantitatively modified so that Donny's individuation can progress."
>
> "Positive prognostic indication is that they were able to work constructively as a family over the course of this year and to resolve at least to some extent their feelings of isolation from each other."
>
> "They seem to have relatively little confidence in their ability to maintain their gains . . . but one had the feeling that the family was able to share more their feelings than act them out."
>
> "Gradually they seemed to develop a sense of interrelatedness with their problems."

As we can see, the judgments were astonishingly accurate. In fact, the observations of the judges were frequently richer than ours, perhaps because they were less cluttered by practical matters brought up at the therapy sessions or by the bickering and mutual accusations so characteristic of this family.

The "blind" judges deepened our understanding of the intricacies of this family's relations and called our attention to additional characteristics in form and organization and whatever had escaped us or was obscured by the distraction of the verbal communication, interaction, etc.

For example, some of the judges noticed more than we did Billy's fragility and immaturity as revealed through his pictures. This may have been overshadowed for us to a degree by Donny's seductively intense psychopathology. We may surmise that Donny's oedipal entanglement with his mother, recognized by all the judges, protected Billy from her overwhelming "Terror and Devastation."

One of the judges inferred that "The separations and changes of therapists which have entered the therapeutic scene seem to have been used as foci for increasing autonomy, more mutuality and cooperation in the family." Thus what we were inclined to see as a liability may have been transformed into an asset.

We were most privileged to have the opinions of such experienced and distinguished psychotherapists. We not only learned much from them about the expressive power of images, but we also gained a more precise understanding of our experience with this family.

SYSTEMATIC STATISTICAL RESEARCH

If we turn now to the systematic computerized statistical type of research aimed at producing results that can be generalized, we must seriously consider the inevitable difficulty of quantification that stems from the very nature of art. Anything that affects the process of creating can make a considerable difference in the art product. There is little likelihood of uniformity in art by different patients or even in art by the same patient. The character of each patient's work depends on his mood, the circumstances preceding the art session, the sessions themselves, or even the introduction of a new medium. Changes in therapeutic relationships also have an influence. Both the form and content of the art products that are the subject of investigation are constantly exposed to these fluctuations. Thus the data are likely to be complex and difficult to interpret.

We must therefore strive for uniformity where uniformity is possible. Any degree of standardization the researcher can introduce is useful. The uniformity gained by the simple expedient of consistently using the same art materials can simplify the process of categorizing the pictures and qualifying their characteristics. Essential too is the consideration of the socioeconomic status, education, intelligence and artistic talent of subjects. In addition, an adequately large sample of subjects, a clear, unambiguous rating manual, and a careful selection and training of judges are necessary.

Statistical studies based on material obtained only from free art expression rather than from carefully designed procedures are likely to be questionable. Even more vulnerable to error is material gathered in group art therapy, where the group process inevitably affects the art products.

Because of its strictly structured format in terms of the tasks and their sequence and the uniform art medium, material from family art evaluations offers the possibility of obtaining good research material. Two studies based on this approach at the Adult Psychiatry Branch of the National Institute of Mental Health may have made a special contribution to the development of an adequate tool for measuring the unusually complex communication inherent in expression through art. Their uniqueness derives from the rare opportunity to have available material as uniform as possible in regard to procedures, media, instructions, setting, participants and investigators.*

---

*Papers aimed at developing adequate tools to measure art productions by mental patients are listed in the bibliography.

THE DENT-KWIATKOWSKA STUDY

The study to be described first, which included 1,514 pictures made by 269 members of 63 families, was made possible by advanced analytic techniques in collaboration with and under the guidance of Dr. James K. Dent. This study will be described as a model for rating material from family art evaluations. Results are still being tabulated and analyzed and will be described in a separate publication.

The Sample

In families participating in this study, the offspring designated as patients presented symptoms of one of a variety of mental disturbances, such as process or reactive schizophrenia, borderline syndromes, character disorders and adjustment reaction to adolescence. Although the socioeconomic status of these families varied, there was a much higher percentage of upper middle-class families than is found in the usual clinical populations. The educational background of the parents ranged from high school to doctoral degrees. Forty-five of the patients were still in high school; nine were in the first year of college, three, in the second year, and four in the third; two had a college degree.

Roughly half of the families were seen in family art evaluation during the first two weeks after admission, and half were seen after a longer period of treatment.

In fifty of the families, the identified patient was hospitalized, and in thirteen he was in outpatient status. The sample also included six families of monozygotic twins. These six families—parents and twins—stayed at the Clinical Center of the National Institutes of Health for two weeks of intensive investigation. In the twin sample the schizophrenic twins came from other hospitals or had been hospitalized earlier.

The majority, approximately 89 percent, of the parents were between forty and sixty years old, but the oldest was seventy-one; the majority, approximately 88 percent, of the identified patients were between fourteen and twenty-six. Children younger than six were excluded from the family art evaluations in this sample.

Our population presented some differences in socioeconomic and educational background and age, but the pictures were produced with the same art medium in the same setting, in a structured session conducted for the most part by the same person. The sample therefore presents an unusual degree of consistency of format and materials.

About 85 percent of the family art evaluations were conducted by me, 5 percent by another art therapist, and 10 percent by psychiatrists well acquainted with the evaluative procedures. However, because of the frequent turnover in personnel, there were almost as many participant-observers as there were families. Since their role was largely passive, we felt that this would not have as much influence on the material obtained as would leadership of the sessions and the giving of instructions by a number of different persons.

The Rating Manual

Devising a manual for rating these pictures was long and arduous. Numerous modifications of the original manual had to be made; many more will be necessary after the preliminary analysis of results obtained so far.*

The items of the rating manual were based on:

1. Salient characteristics observed through the years in pictures by families, one of whose offspring was affected by any one of a variety of psychiatric disturbances. Our material consisted of pictures produced in the course of family art evaluations, and our criteria were specifically designed for the rating of the pictures resulting from the six procedures.
2. The existing literature on features typical of pictures by individuals of different psychopathological groups (see Appendix III).

Most of the ratings describe form, but a few, such as *Comprehensi-*

---

*We are indebted to Doctors Henry Blum, Robert Kaye, Margaret T. Singer, Robert Singer, Hanna K. Ulatowska, and Lyman C. Wynne for their invaluable help in this work.

bility, Meaningfulness of title, Emotional feeling, Pleasing or *Displeasing qualities* and the *Content Code,* deal with the clarity or quality of the communication made by the pictures.

The rating manual we used (Appendix IV) provides for sixty-five columns. The first seventeen card columns identify the number of the study, the subjects, the raters and the procedure. Columns 18 to 41 and 54 to 65 apply to pictures obtained from any of the six procedures of family art evaluations. Items 42 to 53 are not applicable to all procedures; rather, each of them is designed for the rating of certain specific aspects of pictures resulting from each procedure. For example, in regard to family portraits there are such items as *Facial expression, Closeness* and *Isolation,* which are not relevant to other pictures. For the abstract family portraits we rated the *Degree of abstraction,* which again was not applicable when an abstract picture had not been requested. The rating sheet at the end of Appendix IV provides a full list of all items.

Most of the scales begin with zero, meaning "none"; e.g. no color, no jagged lines, no transparency, etc. The number of positions in the scale was determined empirically on the basis of the raters' ability to discriminate. In some cases, like *Number of colors,* the raters could discriminate a fairly large number of colors. In others, like *Emotional feeling,* we had to settle for "none," "little" or "a lot."

Answers to some of the questions in the manual require close visual scrutiny and analysis of a picture but do not call for any subjective reaction. See, for example, Item 22, *Number of colors;* Item 27, *Placement off center;* Item 33, *Coloring in;* Item 41, *Other writing* (besides the title and signature). These items are marked (A). Other items require a response of a more personal, subjective nature. See, for example, Item 18, *Comprehensibility;* Item 56, *Pleasing qualities;* Item 55, *Bizarreness.* These are marked (S).

Preparation of Pictures for Rating

All pictures are made anonymous to eliminate any identification of who drew them. Additionally, while the first item, *Comprehensibility*, is rated, the title of the picture is covered. The cover is then removed and the rater is instructed to look at the picture again to respond to the second item, *Meaningfulness of title;* the title remains uncovered until the end of the rating.

Procedures 1 and 6, free pictures, are all marked 1, so the rater does not know whether he is rating the first or the last picture. The scribble pictures made by individuals (Procedure 4) and jointly by families (Procedure 5) are marked 4 for the same reason.

In both family portraits (Procedures 2 and 3), names of family members are covered; father and mother are identified as "Fa" and "Mo."

All pictures are numbered randomly for identification. The key to the numbers is known only to the person in charge of processing and preparing the pictures for scoring.

The Raters

Forty persons acted as raters, but some ratings were not usable, thus reducing the final number of raters to between twelve and twenty.

Before starting to score, the raters were instructed by one of the investigators. A couple of pictures were jointly rated by them to help clarify rating categories. The first ten pictures of each rater were immediately check-rated by the investigators and discussed with the person who rated them. Thereafter, every fifth picture was check-rated either by one of the investigators or by an experienced rater and the ratings compared. When different responses occurred, they were discussed until agreement was reached. However, four items, *Balance, Bizarreness, Pleasing* and *Displeasing*, were not compared or discussed since we wanted these items to represent the individual judgments of the raters.

Besides the ratings described above, pictures by each individual were looked at together by two judges who had considerable background for art. These judges rated each person's pictures as a whole for artistic talent. A separate rating sheet was designed for this purpose.

It must be emphasized that the study cited did not include interactional material but dealt only with the form and content of pictures. Because this study is still in the process of statistical analysis, this report is limited to the description of the sample and of the rating procedures.

Although the rating manual and systems of analysis were specifically designed for the investigation of material obtained in family art evaluations, our methods can be applied, with certain modifications, for research on artwork obtained by various means from a variety of individuals.

THE TWIN STUDY*

Another rating system was designed for a study on a smaller scale that dealt with material exclusively from the art evaluations of families with identical twins concordant (both twins schizophrenic) or discordant (one twin schizophrenic) for schizophrenia and normal control twins. The study was conducted in collaboration with Dr. Loren R. Mosher,† coauthor of this section.

Here the interactional as well as the pictorial material was included in the rating in an attempt to investigate the quality and style of family transactions and role attribution. Although seventeen families with twins were seen in family art evaluation, this particular analysis served as a pilot study and included only three families: one with normal twins, one in which one twin was schizophrenic, and one in which both twins were schizophrenic.

The section on Twin and Sibling Studies in the Adult Psychiatry Branch of the National Institute of Mental Health studied identical twins and their families for a number of years. The criteria for selection, the study procedures and the preliminary results have been detailed in a number of articles.[25,26,27]

---

*Material used for this section was described in an earlier publication;[5] it was also presented in abbreviated form at the Annual Meeting of the American Psychological Association, Washington, D.C., 1971.

†Chief, Center for Studies of Schizophrenia, Clinical Research Branch, Division of Extramural Research Programs, National Institute of Mental Health.

Each of the twin families was admitted to the Clinical Center of the National Institutes of Health in Bethesda, Maryland, for a two-week period. During this time extensive interviewing, psychological testing and biological determinations were carried out. Family art evaluation was part of the program to assess family psychopathology and interactional patterns.

The material gathered through family art evaluation for the study of families with schizophrenic twins had the same uniformity as that used in the Dent-Kwiatkowska study, reported in the previous section of this chapter, and in some aspects was even more refined. First, the twins were genetically identical and occupied the same chronological space in the family. Second, the family groups participating in the study were always confined to the parents and twins; however, other family members, if any, were usually represented in family pictures, so that we gained a good idea of the family constellations. (In the Dent-Kwiatkowska study the groups varied in size and composition according to the number of participating siblings.) Third, the same investigators, with extensive experience in working together, participated in every art evaluation session. Last, in this study I had no knowledge if a family had one or two schizophrenic twins, who the identified patient (or patients) was, or if it was a normal control family. I also had not had any previous contact with the families or with other investigators who had dealt with them.

The Sample

Of seventeen families with twins seen in family art evaluation, we selected three for comparison: one with twins concordant for schizophrenia, one with twins discordant for schizophrenia, and one in which both twins had no known psychiatric history. One of the reasons for choosing these three families was their being well matched for ability or having had prior artistic experience. In this we were successful, according to the judgment of the raters (see Table III, Variable 6, *Creative resources*).

Table I summarizes the salient characteristics of these families. The normal twins were younger, brighter and better educated than the others. Their parents were also brighter and better

TABLE I

Parental Characteristics by Type of Family	Concordant (Lunissen family)		Discordant (Brown family)		Normal (Stewart family)	
	Father	Mother	Father	Mother	Father	Mother
Age at NIH	60	56	50	53	53	57
Education (yrs.)	4	8	9	8	16	16
Social Class*	IV		IV		II	
Occupation	Small business	Housewife	Small business	Housewife	Engineer	Housewife
IQ (WAIS)	94	105	110	82	127	123

Twin Characteristics by Type of Family	Concordant (Lunissen family)		Discordant (Brown family)		Normal (Stewart family)	
	I†	C	I	C	I†	C
Age at NIH	26	26	26	26	21	21
Age at onset of illness	18	21	24			
Sex	M	M	F	F	F	F
Education (yrs.)	12	12	12	12	15½	15½
Occupation	None	Student	Housewife	Housewife	Student	Student
IQ (WAIS)	83	91	95	93	127	117
Dx	Undif. schizo.	Paranoid schizo.	Resid. schizo.			

* Hollingshead-Redlich.

† In the concordant pair, the "I" is the sicker twin; in the normal pair, the twin of lighter birth weight is designated as "I."

educated than the other parents in the study.

In order to make the figures and numbers in the tables come alive, a brief introduction to the families investigated precedes the account of the methods and results of this study. The data on the families' history were not known to me when I was seeing the families in the art evaluation sessions.

THE LUNISSEN FAMILY, WITH TWINS CONCORDANT FOR SCHIZOPHRENIA. The family consisted of Mr. Lunissen, sixty years old, of rural Scandinavian origin, naturalized American, self-employed; Mrs. Lunissen, fifty-six-year-old housewife; twenty-six-year-old twins, Peter and Paul; twenty-eight-year-old daughter, Mary; and twenty-nine-year-old son, Marc. Mr. and Mrs. Lunissen had been separated for a number of years and lived in different cities. At the time of the separation the children were split between them: The twins and daughter Mary were with the mother, and the father took the oldest son, Marc. By the time of the family art evaluation Mary and Marc had married and established homes of their own. As mentioned, only the twins and their parents participated in the study.

Peter and Paul had both shown increasing signs of emotional stress in late adolescence. Upon admission Peter's diagnosis was schizophrenic reaction, chronic undifferentiated type, and Paul's, paranoid schizophrenia. While Peter had gradually deteriorated and had had a succession of hospitalizations and treatments varying from electro– and insulin shock to milieu and individual psychotherapy, Paul had had fewer psychotic episodes and was functioning at a more adequate level at the time of the evaluation session.

Both Mr. Lunissen's behavior and his pictures were aimed at proclaiming himself leader of the family. His strongly drawn representation of himself in a picture of the family occupies half of the paper and is inscribed with his full name in huge letters (Fig. 100). He differentiates little among the beaked faces of the family members, shown cut off just below the neck. No one acknowledged his leadership during the session, and much of his attempt to lead was foiled by his own disorganized behavior. In most of his drawings, too, he mixed various unconnected themes and was rarely able to convey a coherent meaning. As we see in Figure 101, he was unable to integrate his scribble into any kind of unified picture but inscribed each of the various shapes "Balloon," "Vase" and "Figer eight" (sic) without attempting to find any connection between them.

Mrs. Lunissen's behavior in the art evaluation session was reflected in her artwork. Her remarks were usually unclear, her thoughts often seemed unconnected, and, like her husband, she did not seem to differentiate between the twins. Her pictures are empty and vague, and their elements lack connection with one another. Her family portrait reveals four sexless, practically bodiless figures, which she globally inscribed "children." Indeed, she said she saw her offspring simply as a "group of children" without any difference among them (Fig. 102).

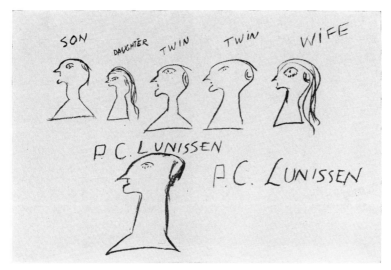

Figure 100.

Figure 101.

Throughout the session Mr. and Mrs. Lunissen seemed to be covertly angry with each other.

The twins' productions and behavior were quite dissimilar.

Peter, the sicker twin, seemed to seek support from his brother and frequently waited for words of encouragement that Paul was either unwilling or, more probably, unable to give. Throughout

Figure 102.

the session Peter's performance was rather fixed, dull and frequently irrelevant. His lack of motivation was obvious. We see a minimal effort and a lack of integration in his individual scribble picture (Fig. 103).

Paul was functioning adequately in the community at the time of the session. His first picture, "Tropical Winter" (Plate XII), shows some organization and investment and even a certain richness of color and texture. But his work deteriorated considerably whenever it touched upon emotionally charged material, as we can see in his picture of the family (Fig. 104). The figures, which are all drawn in red, are vague; they lack detail and are faceless. His mother and sister are depicted with hands, but all the males have none. He and his twin are nondifferentiated; they are close to each other and are the smallest of the group.

In the joint scribble, "Sea Adventure" (Fig. 105), Peter made his first assertive foray. The other family members were engaged in a fierce struggle to force their own ideas, and Paul finally outlined a shark. Peter then quietly drew a huge buoy that dominates the picture and detracts from the shark. Later, when his

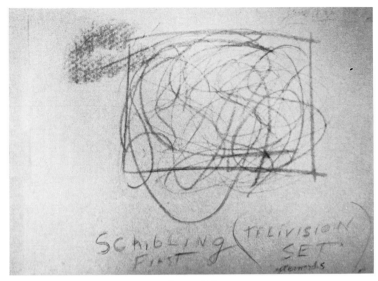

Figure 103.

father and brother cut him down, he withdrew from discussing title and signatures.

Figure 104.

THE BROWN FAMILY, WITH TWINS DISCORDANT FOR SCHIZO-PHRENIA. The Brown family consisted of father, age fifty; mother,

Figure 105.

age fifty-three; and the twins, Janet and Jenny, age twenty-six, both married. There were three other siblings.

Mr. and Mrs. Brown had worked hard for many years. Mr. Brown had recently managed to retire from his own small business and had a steady income adequate for himself and his wife. He looked younger than his age and was physically vigorous. The other investigators who interviewed him saw him as easygoing, rather strong and independent.

Mrs. Brown came from a rural background. Throughout her life she had had a number of somatic complaints. She was extremely phobic, had had an episode of hysteric blindness, and at the time of her admission to the National Institute of Mental Health complained of severe migraine-like headaches.

While at the National Institute of Mental Health, Mrs. Brown was initially uncooperative and had a rather negative attitude toward the study. This gradually changed and she was pleased that all her many complaints were carefully looked into. However, most of the investigators continued to see her as a suspicious, hypochondriacal, selfish and demanding person.

Janet, the schizophrenic twin, was the mother of three, ages six, three and one and one-half. Throughout her life she had had a tendency to withdraw and to have crying spells. She had also had a volatile temper. Until about fourteen months before her admission to the twin project, however, she had had no overt psychotic symptoms. In the preceding year she had been hospitalized for several brief periods. The crises were precipitated by the imminent separation from her parental family because her husband's firm had chosen him for an overseas assignment. Her relationship with her husband had also deteriorated, perhaps in part because of her reluctance to go abroad with him. Her behavior became so uncontrolled and bizarre that her husband finally realized that she was sick and, with her consent, took her to the hospital. Between her hospitalizations Janet was able to function adequately. While she was at the National Institute of Mental Health, she had no psychotic symptoms.

Jenny, the control twin, was also the mother of three. She had no history of psychiatric disorder; extensive psychological examination showed no serious defects. She was pleasant and cooperative throughout her hospital stay.

During the family art evaluation the Brown parents had many angry exchanges, but their style of battle was different from that of the Lunissen family in that their hostility was direct, not subtle and covert.

Mr. Brown appeared quite different in the family art evaluation situation from the way he was otherwise seen. He was uninterested in the procedures and withdrew from the family throughout the session. He seemed to wish only to get it over with and showed no interest in feelings expressed by him or others. His pictures had little content and consisted mostly of unrelated elements; see, for example, his first free picture (Fig. 106).

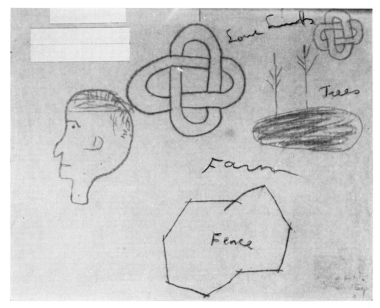

Figure 106.

Mrs. Brown's attitude during the family art evaluation was more consistent with her usual behavior. She appeared quite depressed and was self-deprecatory. Her pictures were concrete and somewhat bizarre; she had difficulty organizing a coherent picture. While she displayed little interest in the twins, she seemed to be somewhat more involved with Janet, the twin who was diagnosed schizophrenic.

The twins were quite invested in the procedure and took great pride in what they did. They maintained a warm relationship, and Jenny obviously led Janet constructively, in contrast with what went on between the Lunissen twins.

Janet, the schizophrenic twin, seemed to look to other family members, especially her twin and, to a lesser extent, her mother, for guidance and ideas. Her pictures, when not modeled on her sister's, carried some of the bizarreness of her mother's very crude productions; for example, Figure 34 shown in Chapter VII.

Jenny, the normal twin, was somewhat preoccupied with the organization and accuracy of her work (see Figure 35, Chapter VII). She was very supportive of her sister, however.

Both twins' pictures were colorful, although Janet's were not as well organized as Jenny's and were more concrete. Some of the other productions of the two were remarkably similar; Janet obviously looked up to Jenny, and we can assume that she was imitating her sister rather than making her own choices.

On the group task, "Baby Carriage" (Fig. 107), this family had great difficulty in deciding whose scribble to complete. Mrs. Brown was by far the most active and controlling in the making of the decision. However, when what was first seen by her as a "Racing Car" was perceived by Mr. Brown as a "Baby Carriage," she gave in and went along with his choice of subject and title. The reversal of the most commonly expected male-female associations is interesting. It may shed light in the real nature of their relationship and roles in the family.

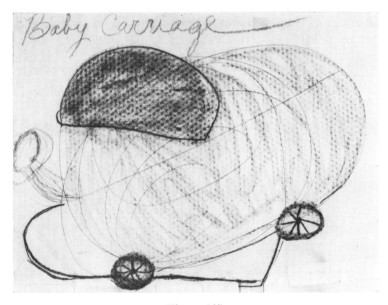

Figure 107.

THE STEWART FAMILY, WITH NORMAL CONTROL TWINS. The control family consisted of father, age fifty-three; mother, age fifty-seven; and twin daughters, Rosalyn and Rosemary, age twenty-one. There were no other siblings in the family. None of the four members of this family had had psychiatric difficulties requiring treatment.

Mr. Stewart had just changed jobs and was going through a difficult period of adjustment to a new assignment. He was rather withdrawn, maybe on the depressive side, but was fighting depression by engaging in various hobbies. Mrs. Stewart appeared to be more aggressive than he and to have a tendency to control others. She smiled in a benevolent fashion most of the time and covered her domineering tendency with a kind of humor.

Both girls were college graduates and were well adjusted. They mentioned having some problems but being able to handle them successfully. Both were about to separate from the parental family, Rosalyn through the start of a professional career, and Rosemary through an approaching marriage. Rosalyn was like mother and Rosemary was rather like father; indeed, each twin seemed to pair off with the parent she emulated.

Mr. Stewart's pictures were of rather poor quality, but he was able to see and explain their meaning. His abstract family portrait (Fig. 108), although far from symbolic abstraction, expresses his feeling about the imminent separation from his daughters, each of whom was going her own way.

Figure 108.

We noted that although Mrs. Stewart's drawings, like those of her husband, were of exceptionally poor quality, she was able to supplement her pictures with very clear comments on the feelings and events they stood for. Her abstract family portrait (Fig. 109) looks vague and indefinite; however, she is able to convey through her comments the symbolism of her drawing, expressing how she views the family. She represents the family as united in love and sheltered from life's difficulties by a "solid core background." In general, although she did control the girls to some extent during the session, she played a passive-submissive role vis-à-vis her husband; he was clearly designated as the leader in the family.

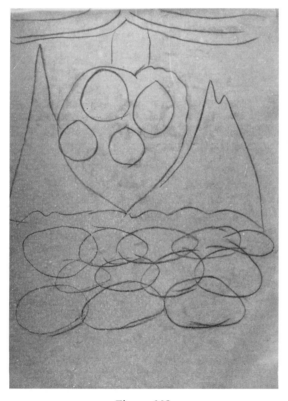

Figure 109.

During the session the twins appeared quite different from each other, both in their behavior and in what they portrayed. Rosalyn was active, talkative and ebullient, while Rosemary was rather taciturn and slightly withdrawn.

Rosalyn was action oriented; her pictures express motion. Her picture "Blue Bird Silver Tail" (Fig. 110) is a family portrait. Through this lively picture she represents the family's experience of travel in a trailer. It is significant that she shows her sister driving off with father while she herself goes another way with mother.

Rosemary's pictures are more rigid and stereotyped; see, for example, Figure 111, a picture of the family. But her figures are complete and not particularly distorted; sexes and persons are well differentiated.

On the group task the family performed well. Each made a sortie as leader, but it was father who eventually made the decision. On the whole, this family's interactions were warm and lively, and the "Owl" (Fig. 112), produced jointly, was well integrated and expressive.

Figure 110.

Figure 111.

The Rating Manual*

The criteria in this study were based on the investigators' past experience with artwork by families with schizophrenic twins.

The study focused on:

1. *Individual evaluation:* The personality and relational style of each family member.
2. *Intrafamily comparison:* The ways in which the individuals interrelate within one family.
3. *Interfamily comparison:* The comparison, through their art production, of families in which both twins are schizophrenic, one twin is schizophrenic, or neither twin is schizophrenic.
4. *The specific study of twinship.*

---

*See Appendix V.

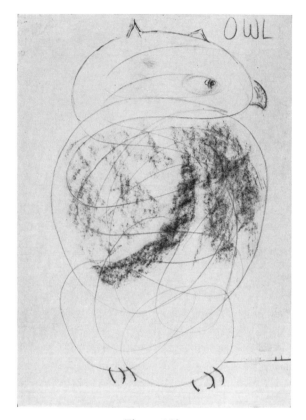

Figure 112.

The Ratings

Two "blind" raters scored on twelve variables the material obtained in family art evaluation with the three selected families. Individual and family names were covered and pictures were either randomly arranged for scoring on certain variables or arranged by sets of pictures of each individual or family for scoring other variables.

The written descriptive abstracts of the sessions were edited so that no diagnostic inferences could be detected.

Ratings of all variables were done on 5-point scales with 5 representing the least adequate performance in each instance.

Each variable was scored by two raters.

The material was divided into four sections for the ratings. Satisfactory interrater reliabilities were obtained for each section (see Table II).

TABLE II

Intraclass Correlation Coefficients (Two Raters)

	F	r	p
Section I	9.021	.80	$<.01$
Section II	6.2261	.72	$<.01$
Section III	4.6060	.64	$<.01$
Section IV	5.4284	.69	$<.01$

Section I

The first and last free pictures and individual scribbles of all members of the three families (thirty-six pictures in all) were arranged randomly and each was rated on the following three variables:

1. *Integration:* How well the components are arranged into a meaningful whole.
2. *Understandability:* How understandable the picture is.
3. *Use of colors:* Number of colors used.

Section II

4. *Body image:* The twelve family portraits were randomly arranged and each figure represented in the pictures was rated on this variable.
5. *Level of abstraction:* The twelve abstract family portraits, also randomly arranged, were each rated for this variable.

Section III

6. *Creative resources:* Each person's first and last pictures and individual scribble pictures were rated in sets of three pictures for each of the twelve family members for degree of rater-judged imaginativeness and expressiveness.

Section IV

The three families' joint pictures started with the help of a scribble were rated in conjunction with the edited summaries of the entire sessions for family group performance.

The variables in this section were:

7. *Subjective responses of raters:* Subjective responses of rater to picture and to behavior throughout the session; 1 = positive; 5 = negative.

8. *Interactional quality of family members:* 1 = positive, constructive interaction; 5 = uncooperative, perfunctory interaction.

9. *Individuation:* 1 = independence with communication; 5 = extreme interdependence or complete isolation.

10. *Involvement:* 1 = positive interaction and rapport; 5 = withdrawal.

11. *Alliances:* 1 = solid positive alliances; 5 = no alliances or hostile ones.

12. *Ability to work on joint task:* Ability of the family to focus attention on the task, to follow instructions, and jointly to produce a complete picture. 1 = organized, well-integrated picture; 5 = unable to complete the task.

The ratings of Section IV were designed as an attempt to look at the quality and style of family interaction and role attribution.

Examples of Scores

The following examples illustrate some of the extreme scores.

Section I

1. *Integration:* Figure 101 (X rating = 4.5), the individual scribble by the Lunissen father, shows a poorly organized picture of unrelated parts; on the other end of the scale, Figure 35, "Country Scene," the first picture by the non-schizophrenic twin in the Brown family, transmits a sense of organization and unity (X rating = 1).

2. *Understandability:* Figure 113 (X rating = 5), the individual scribble by the Lunissen mother, is essentially incomprehensible. In contrast, Figure 35 mentioned above conveys clearly content and meaning (X rating = 1).

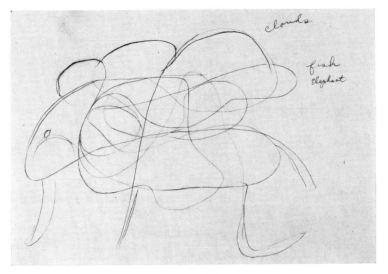

Figure 113.

Section II

4. *Body image:* In the family portrait, Figure 100 (X rating = 4.5), by the Lunissen father, the bodies are not represented despite instructions requesting the whole figure; the heads also show considerable distortion. Figure 110, "Blue Bird Silver Tail" (X rating = 1.5), by one of the normal twins, portrays a family by means of complete and undistorted figures.

5. *Level of abstraction:* In Figure 109 (X rating = 1), this abstract family portrait shows the capacity of the Stewart mother to depict feelings and personalities in a nonrepresentational way. On the other hand, Figure 108 (X rating = 4), drawn by her husband, demonstrates his considerable difficulty in representing personalities or relationships abstractly.

Section III

6. *Creative resources:* Figure 35, by the control twin in the Brown family, was responsible for her mean rating of 1 on this variable. However, because of the somewhat barren

quality of Mrs. Brown's first individual picture (not shown) her mean rating on this variable was 4.5.

Section IV

12. *Ability to work on joint task:* Striking examples of various degrees of ability to work on a joint task are provided by the joint scribble pictures by the three families. The Lunissen family's "Sea Adventure" (Fig. 105) received a rating of 5; the Brown family's "Baby Carriage" (Fig. 107) received a rating of 4; and the Stewart family's "Owl" (Fig. 112) received a rating of 2. Our blind raters thus indicated that they saw the Lunissen family as having only hostile, negative alliances and the Stewart family as having generally solid, positive ones.

Results

One would be inclined to hypothesize that the family scoring best would be the Stewart family (normal) and the family scoring worst would be the Lunissen family (concordant). But according to the tables, we obtain only a partial confirmation of this hypothesis.

We see in Table III a consistent difference in the individual means between the parents of the twins with no, one, or two psychologically abnormal twin offspring. The parents in the Stewart family, whose twins were normal, performed better than did the parents in the Brown family, whose twins were discordant for schizophrenia. The Brown parents in turn scored better than did the Lunissen parents of twins concordant for schizophrenia. However, this consistency was not found in the twins' scores, as we see from Table III and examples of their ratings.

It is noteworthy that on the variables in Section I, *Integration, Understandability,* and *Use of color,* the twins in the discordant pair performed as well as the normals did, whereas the concordant twins performed less well. In general, the twins as a group performed better than their parents did.

Section II contained two variables, *Body image* and *Level of abstraction.* Each person represented in the pictures was scored

TABLE III

Variable*	Section I. Ratings of Each First and Last Free Picture and Individual Scribbles (36 Pictures)						
	Mother	Father	Parental total	I†	C†	Twin total	Family total
1. Integration							
N	2.00	1.75	3.75	1.75	2.50	4.25	8.00
D	3.00	3.25	6.25	2.25	2.50	4.75	11.00
C	3.50	3.67	7.17	3.17	2.50	5.67	12.84
2. Understandability							
N	1.50	1.00	2.50	1.50	1.75	3.25	5.75
D	3.25	3.25	6.50	2.25	1.75	4.00	10.50
C	2.83	4.20	7.03	3.50	2.33	5.83	12.86
3. Use of color							
N	3.75	4.75	8.50	2.75	2.75	5.50	14.00
D	3.00	3.25	6.25	1.50	1.75	3.25	9.50
C	3.67	2.67	6.34	4.17	3.33	7.50	13.84
Overall totals							
N			14.75			13.00	27.75
D			19.00			12.00	31.00
C			20.54			19.00	39.54

Variable*	Section II. Ratings of Each Family Portrait (12 Pictures) and Each Abstract Family Portrait (12 Pictures)						
	Mother	Father	Parental total	I†	C†	Twin total	Family total
4. Body image							
N	1.50	1.37	2.87	1.50	1.50	3.00	5.87
D	4.36	1.75	6.11	2.50	2.50	5.00	11.11
C	3.42	4.50	7.92	3.58	5.00	8.58	16.50
5. Abstraction							
N	1.00 §	4.00	5.00	5.00	4.50	9.50	14.50
D	2.00	4.00	6.00	4.50	1.50	6.00	12.00
C	2.50	1.00	3.50	5.00	1.00	6.00	9.50
Overall totals							
N			7.87			12.50	20.37
D			12.11			11.00	23.11
C			11.42			14.58	26.00

Variable*	Section III. Ratings of Each Individual's Set of First and Last Free Pictures and Individual Scribbles (12 Sets of 3 Pictures)						
	Mother	Father	Parental total	I†	C†	Twin total	Family total
6. Creative resources							
N	3.50	3.50	7.00	3.00	3.50	6.50	13.50
D	4.50	4.00	8.50	2.00	1.00	3.00	11.50
C	4.50	4.50	9.00	3.50	2.50	6.00	15.00

Variable	Section IV. Ratings of Each Joint Scribble with Narrative Summary (3 Pictures)		
	＼ Stewart family	Brown family	Lunissen family
7. Rater response	3.00	4.00	4.50
8. Interaction	3.00	3.50	4.50
9. Individuation	3.00	3.00	4.50
10. Involvement	2.00	4.00	5.00
11. Alliances	2.00	3.50	5.00
12. Task focus	1.50	3.00	3.00
Total	14.50	21.00	26.50

* In each case, a higher number is indicative of a less adequate performance. Each number is the mean of two ratings.

† In the concordant pair, the "I" is the sicker twin; in the normal pair, the twin of lighter birth weight is designated as "I."

In the variable column, N (Normal) designates the Stewart family; D (discordant), the Brown family; and C (concordant), the Lunissen family.

§ Based on only one rating.

separately for *Body image*. The scores for *Level of abstraction* were derived from only one rating of each abstract family portrait. Because the means on *Body image* might represent as many as six individual scores, the two are reported separately. The individual mean scores for *Body image* distinguished between the three types of families without overlap. The Brown mother, who was rated in another study[26] as clinically close to her schizophrenic daughter, did substantially worse than her spouse did. Her score was more like that of both parents in the Lunissen family. In the Lunissen family the sicker twin's performance on the *Body image* variable was rated slightly better than his twin's. These consistent differences were not found on *Levels of abstraction*. Since these means were derived from so few ratings, we hesitate to define them as conclusive.

Section III contained only one variable, *Creative resources.* Each individual's first and last free pictures and individual scribble picture were arranged as a set. The raters were not told what type of family the individual was a member of or what his place in the family was, e.g. father, psychopathological twin, etc. Again the parents of the normal twins did better than those of the pairs with recognized psychopathology did. However, despite the greater intelligence of the normal twins, their score was higher (less adequate) than the score of the less sick twin in the concordant pair. The generally high scores on this variable indicate that we were successful in our attempt to match the three families for talent.

Section IV contained a complex series of ratings on six variables (7 to 12) : *Subjective response of the rater, Interactional quality, Individuation, Involvement, Alliances,* and *Ability to work on a joint task.* The entire family received a single score for each variable. These scores were based on the blinded written description of family interaction during the joint scribble and on the picture itself. As may be seen in Table III, the mean family ratings for Variables 7 to 12 clearly distinguished between the three types of families.

When one looks at the family totals by individuals for all variables, great consistency is found in the parents' scores; there is a stepwise progression from the normal to the discordant to the concordant parents. In the twins, however, the total scores for the discordant pair are not very different from those of the normal pair, despite the greater socioeconomic, intellectual and educational resources of the latter.

The three sets of parents were generally more differentiated than were the three sets of twins. Specifically, Variables 1 *(Integration)*, 2 *(Understandability)*, and 4 *(Body image)* discriminated between the three sets of parents. For the twins, only Variables 2 and 4 distinguished between the three levels of psychopathology.

The family interaction Variables 7 to 12, derived principally from the family study literature, proved to be powerful discriminators in our study. The raters, who worked with abstracts of sessions that were blinded and therefore knew nothing of the diagnostic status of the families, were able to distinguish, without overlap, between the levels of pathology represented in these families.

As may be seen in Table III, the parents received generally higher (less adequate) scores on most variables than did the twins. Their ratings were consistent with our expectations, in that on most variables the parents of the concordant twins did most poorly and the parents of the control twins did best.

A number of the conclusions about the twins, however, were surprising; they did not confirm our initial expectations. First, on the variables in Section I, the performance of the discordant pair was similar to that of the normal pair; it was not poorer as we had expected. Second, the *Level of abstraction* of both normal twins was rated as identical to that of both identified patients in the families with twins concordant and discordant for schizophrenia. And third, the *Creative resources* of the normal twins were rated even worse than those of the identified patients in the psychopathological pair of twins.

How may we account for these puzzling results of the twins' performance? Because we noted striking differences in the ways the three sets of twins interacted, we speculate that something in their relationships may account for the results.

In the concordant pair, the less sick twin was hostile and gave no support to his brother. This behavior was not consistent with the past, for the two brothers had earlier been close and helpful to each other. Perhaps the less sick twin was afraid of being identified with his brother, of becoming as sick as he was, and of having to spend years in hospitals; this fear may have led to his hostility toward and rejection of his brother. Throughout most of the procedures, the sicker twin scored very poorly. The possibility must be considered that the rejecting attitude of his healthier twin lowered the level of his performance.

In the discordant pair of twins, the nonschizophrenic twin was supportive of her schizophrenic sister. Throughout the session she seemed, with her warm attitude, to lead and encourage her. This behavior was consistent with that of the past, since the twins had remained in close contact with each other even after both were married. In the art evaluation session the sick twin often followed and imitated her sister's work and ideas. The support and leadership she received from her normal sister may have raised the level of her performance above what it might otherwise have been, which may account for the similarity in their scores. However, the sick twin also at times sought her mother's support; clinically, she was closer to her mother than to her twin sister. This may have led to the bizarreness noted in some of her pictures, similar to that observed in her mother's pictures.

As in the discordant pair, the normal twins were supportive of each other, with one clearly leading the other. The normal twins, however, communicated with each other much more overtly. Their scores were for the most part similar.

Conclusion

In general this study reflects important family processes. Organization of thoughts, feelings and modes of interaction were reflected in the artwork. In the pictures of the family with normal twins, love, warmth, and clarity of communication seemed to be revealed; this was confirmed by their verbal interpretations of the pictures. In the families with schizophrenic offspring, emptiness, vagueness, lack of focus on the task, and lack of distinctness seemed to be portrayed. Indeed, this was how the family members interacted during the art evaluation sessions: with warmth in the normal family; with covert anger in the family with two schizophrenic offspring; and with direct hostility between the parents in the family with one schizophrenic offspring.

This pilot study demonstrates the possibility of a standardized, reliable method of scoring for the use of art procedures toward further understanding of relations in families with a schizophrenic member. The study holds promise, but its results need confirmation through analysis of a larger sample.

CONCLUDING REMARKS

I N THIS BOOK I have tried to collect and report experiences that I found particularly illuminating and from which I learned most in the years of my work with families. I hope my efforts will be of assistance to those engaged in helping distressed families to communicate through art.

I am extremely rewarded by the fact that a number of my colleagues are now engaged in the investigation and treatment of families by means of art.

As in any new field, a variety of approaches and techniques are being applied and experimented with. They differ depending on the therapist's personal orientation, the program and the type of patient population of the institution with which the therapist is affiliated. But all bring an important contribution to the understanding of the family process.

Writing this book was for me a journey through memories of powerful experiences and emotions. The journey was long and at times arduous. How to translate into an easily readable form all the intricacies of work with whole systems of relationships? Relationships that are unclear, complicated, desperate in an unsuccessful effort by family members to reach one another, or reluctant to do so out of fear of the pain associated with feeling.

In the first part of the book I reached back to my first encounters with families when I started to perceive that words may be too definite, and too concrete or final to express feelings that are either beyond awareness or unclearly formulated.

The accidental discovery that expression through art may open new avenues of communication between family members as well as between families and therapists was a revelation. It aroused my interest in the further exploration of how best to use this new tool.

From the groping in the dark of the first years, techniques and

214

theoretical concepts gradually started to emerge. On the other hand I was discovering in the families' artwork and in their behavior while producing them a striking illustration of the existing theories on family systems and relations in a variety of diagnostic groups.

The first chapters of the book describe initial discoveries that led to the development of techniques, with therapeutic or evaluative objectives, for graphic communication among family members.

I chose for clinical examples material that impressed me most in my work with families. As vividly as this material remained implanted in my memory, while reviewing it I saw in the pictures messages I had not been aware of while actively engaged in work with the families. The image itself seems to be the most eloquent spokesman for the inner human experience. This is confirmed by the results of the study on "blind" evaluation of pictures in family art therapy described in Chapter X.

However, I also understood the danger of relying solely on subjective reaction in building any solid theoretical formulation. The last two sections of Chapter X and the statistical methods they describe will, I hope, be helpful in providing art therapists with methods for scientific investigation of as difficult an endeavor as measuring art, by itself and in combination with the intricacy of family psychopathology. The methods may be fallible; many more experimental studies are needed. But at least a start was made. These methods may also be another step in the efforts to reinforce for art therapy a respected position in the psychotherapeutic domain.

APPENDICES

APPENDIX I:

1. *The Setting* — Hospital or other institution; part of a regular program or experimental procedure.
2. *The Family* — a. Names, age and sex of participating family members (give same for nonparticipating family members).
   b. Brief description of physical appearance.
   c. Socioeconomic and educational background.
   d. Reason for referral.
   e. How was the family prepared for the session.
3. *Special Circumstances* —
   a. What happened just before the session? Or any other factor that may be of influence on the pictures and/or family behavior.
   b. Your own position; leader, participant member, staff member, acquaintance. Include your pre-session mood.
4. *The Art Productions* —
   a. Number of each procedure.
   b. Name of each family member.
   c. Title of each picture.
   d. Brief description of significant aspects of each picture.
   e. Comments by family members and your own remarks.
5. *Group Process* — General observations on the family dynamics based on pictures and family interactions; shifts in organization of the group: splits, alliances, domination, submission, leadership, etc.

6. *Notable Observations* — Tentative conclusions and diagnostic impressions based on pictures and family transactions. Focal conflict and attempted solutions. Include historical data obtained during the session.

7. *Subjective Reaction* — Your personal feelings during and after this session. Include major points by-passed intentionally or unintentionally.

8. *Problems and Difficulties You Encountered.*

PLEASE REMEMBER TO DISGUISE THE FAMILY
MEMBERS' IDENTITY

APPENDIX II:

ART THERAPY EDUCATION — APRIL 1976

Notes: The Education Committee of the American Art Therapy Association has prepared this list for information only.   Listing constitutes neither approval on the part of the organization, nor a guarantee that any set of educational standards has been met.   An updated list of programs offered by institutions is available in April and October of each year.

Information about financial assistance must be obtained from the individual institutions listed.

U.S. and CANADIAN INSTITUTIONS

GRADUATE PROGRAMS

THE ART PSYCHOTHERAPY INSTITUTE OF CLEVE-LAND (formerly the Cleveland Institute of Art Psychotherapy), 2800 Mayfield Road, #202, Cleveland Heights, OH 44118. (Contact: Pamela Diamond, ATR, Director)
   One-Year Program in Art Psychotherapy.   Certificate.

CALIFORNIA STATE UNIVERSITY, SACRAMENTO, 6000 J Street, Sacramento, CA 95819.   (Contact: Prof. Donald M. Uhlin, Ed. D., ATR, Department of Art)
   Master of Arts in Art with Emphasis in Art Therapy.

CREATIVE ARTS THERAPIES ASSOCIATION TRAINING INSTITUTE, 54 West Ninth Street, New York, NY 10011. (Contact: Steve Ross, ATR)
   Two-Year Program.   Certificate of Completion.

EASTERN VIRGINIA MEDICAL SCHOOL, Norfolk, VA 23507. (Contact: Ronald E. Hays, ATR, Director of Adjunctive Therapies, Norfolk Community Mental Health Center, 721 Fairfax Avenue, Norfolk, VA 23507)

Certificate of Completion.

EMPORIA KANSAS STATE COLLEGE, 1200 Commercial Street, Emporia, KS 66801. (Contact: Dal H. Cass, Chairman, Psychology Department)

Master of Science in Art Therapy.

The GEORGE WASHINGTON UNIVERSITY, Graduate School of Arts and Sciences, Bacon Hall #201, Washington, DC 20052. (Contact: Dean of the Graduate School of Arts and Sciences)

Master of Arts in Art Therapy.

GODDARD COLLEGE, Plainfield, VT 05667. (Contact: Graduate Program Admissions Office, Attention Gladys L. Agell, ATR)

15 Month Program, 2 Summers On Campus, 9 Months in the Field.

Master of Arts Degree in Art Therapy.

GODDARD COLLEGE, Plainfield, VT 05667. (Contact: Graduate Program Admissions Office)

Master of Arts Degree through Individualized Studies in Art Therapy (and other fields), pursued at any approved location.

HAHNEMANN MEDICAL COLLEGE, Department of Mental Health Sciences, New College Building, 230 North Broad Street, Philadelphia, PA 19102. (Contact: Mrs. Myra Levick, Director, Adjunctive Therapies Education)

Master of Creative Arts in Therapy (MCAT) with specializations in Art Therapy, Movement Therapy, and Music Therapy.

IMMACULATE HEART COLLEGE, 2021 N. Western Avenue, Los Angeles, CA 90027. (Contact: Office of the Graduate School)

Master of Arts in Art Therapy.

LESLEY COLLEGE, Institute for the Arts and Human Development, Cambridge, MA 02138. (Contact: Shaun A. McNiff, Graduate School of Education)

Master of Education in Art Therapy and Other Creative Therapies.

LINDENWOOD 4, THE LINDENWOOD COLLEGES, St.

Charles, MO, St. Louis, MO, Washington, D.C., Santa Monica, CA. (Contact: D. Cohen, M.F.A., P. Eisendrath, M.A., or P. Glick, M.A., ATR, Lindenwood 4, 4635 Maryland Ave. St. Louis, MO 63108)

Master of Arts in Art Therapy through Individualized Study Programs at any of the above locations.

LONE MOUNTAIN COLLEGE, 2800 Turk Boulevard, San Francisco, CA 94118. (Contact: Joanne G. Harris, Ph.D., Director, Creative Arts Therapy Program)

Master of Arts in Creative Arts Therapy with Emphasis in Art, Music or Dance.

UNIVERSITY OF LOUISVILLE, Institute of the Expressive Therapies, Louisville, KY 40202. (Contact: Sandra L. Kagin, ATR, Director)

Master of Arts in Art Therapy, Dance Therapy, and Drama Therapy.

MASSACHUSETTS COLLEGE OF ART, 364 Brookline Avenue, Boston, MA 02215. (Contact: Dr. Dorothy Simpson, Director, Graduate and Continuing Education)

Master of Science in Art Education with a Specialization in Art Therapy.

MONTCLAIR STATE COLLEGE, Upper Montclair, NJ 07043. (Contact: Professor Susan E. Gonick-Barris, ATR, Director, Graduate Studies in Art Therapy, Fine Arts Department)

Masters Degree in Art Education with a Concentration in Art Therapy.

COLLEGE OF NEW ROCHELLE, New Rochelle, NY 10801. (Contact: Chairman, Graduate Program in Art Education)

Master of Arts in Art Education with an Option in Therapeutic Techniques in Art Education.

NEW YORK UNIVERSITY, 80 Washington Square East, New York, NY 10003. (Contact: Laurie Wilson, ATR, Coordinator Art Therapy Program, Department of Art Education)

Master of Arts Degree.

PRATT INSTITUTE, 125 Higgins Hall, Brooklyn, NY 11205.

(Contact: Josef E. Garai, Ph.D., ATR, Director of Art Therapy)
Master of Professional Studies in Art Therapy and Creativity
Development.

TEMPLE UNIVERSITY, Department of Recreation and Leisure Studies, College of HPERD, Philadelphia, PA 19140. (Contact: Bonnie Klein, Temple University Hospital, Psychiatric Inpatient Unit, 2 Main South, Broad and Ontario Streets, Philadelphia, PA 19140)
Master's Degree in Therapeutic Activities — Art Therapy.

WRIGHT STATE UNIVERSITY, Dayton, OH 45431. (Contact: Dr. Gary Barlow, ATR, Professor and Coordinator, Art Education, 326 Creative Arts Building)
Master's Degree in Art Education with a Concentration in Art Therapy.

CLINICAL TRAINING PROGRAMS

BETHESDA HOSPITAL, 2951 Maple Avenue, Zanesville, OH 43701. (Contact: Bernard O. Stone, ATR, MFA, Director, Art Psychotherapy Department)
Eight-Week Graduate Interims. Spring, Summer, Fall and Winter.

ESSEX COUNTY HOSPITAL CENTER, Department of Music and Creative Art Therapies, Box 500, Cedar Grove, NJ 07009. (Contact: Sandra C. Golden, RMT, Director, Music and Creative Art Therapies)
Six-Month Affiliation. Certificate.

HIGHLAND VIEW HOSPITAL — ART STUDIO, 3901 Ireland Drive, Cleveland, OH 44122. (Contact: Ms. Mickie McGraw, Director)
Clinical experience at undergraduate and graduate levels through accredited colleges.

UNIVERSITY OF MARYLAND, College Park, MD 20742. (Contact: Professor Harold McWhinnie, Crafts Department, College of Human Ecology)
Field Work, Internships in Conjunction with Art Education and Crafts Courses.

MILWAUKEE PSYCHIATRIC HOSPITAL, 1220 Dewey Avenue, Wauwatosa, WI 53213. (Contact: Bill Smith, Director, Education, Vocation, and Recreation)
Six-Month Internship. Certificate.

NORTHWESTERN INSTITUTE OF PSYCHIATRY. Lafayette Avenue and Bethlehem Pike, Fort Washington, PA 19034. (Contact: Lea Camero, Art Therapist, Department of Adjunctive Therapy)
Six-Month Practicum.

SAINT ELIZABETHS HOSPITAL, Washington, D.C. 20032. (Contact: Anne K. Bushart, Chief, Recreational Therapy Section)
Clinical experience at undergraduate and graduate levels through accredited colleges.

CAPITAL UNIVERSITY, Columbus, Ohio 43209.
Undergraduate with nine-month clinical practicum.

HARDING HOSPITAL, Worthington, Ohio 43087. (Contact: Don Jones, ATR)
Graduate level.

SPECIAL PROGRAMS

GESTALT INSTITUTE OF CHICAGO, 609 Davis Street, Evanston, IL 60201. (Contact: Charlotte Rosner, Chairperson, Post-Graduate Training Faculty)

HOME FOR CRIPPLED CHILDREN: REGIONAL COMPREHENSIVE REHABILITATION CENTER FOR CHILDREN AND YOUTH, 1426 Denniston Avenue, Pittsburgh, PA 15217. (Contact: Roberta Davis, ATR, 1322 Squirrel Hill Avenue, Pittsburgh, PA 15217)

TORONTO ART THERAPY INSTITUTE, 216 St. Clair Avenue, West, Toronto, Ontario, Canada. (Contact: Martin A. Fischer, M.D., D. Psych., Executive Director)

UNDERGRADUATE PROGRAMS

ALBERTUS MAGNUS COLLEGE, New Haven, CT 06511. (Contact: Chairman, Art Department or Chairman, Psychology Department)

Major in Art or Psychology with an Emphasis in Art Therapy.

UNIVERSITY OF BRIDGEPORT. See Junior College of Connecticut.

CAPITAL UNIVERSITY, 2199 E. Main Street, Columbus, OH 43209. (Contact: Professor Richard Phipps, Chairman, Art Department)
Major in Art with an Emphasis in Psychology and Internship in Art Therapy.

DEAN JUNIOR COLLEGE, Franklin, MA 02038. (Contact: Director of Admissions)
Associate in Science, with a Major in Art Therapy.

UNIVERSITY OF EVANSVILLE, P.O. Box 329, Evansville, IN 44702. (Contact: Mr. Leslie Miley, Jr., Chairman, Department of Art)
Bachelor of Science in Art and Associated Studies with a Major in Art Therapy.

JUNIOR COLLEGE OF CONNECTICUT, University of Connecticut, Bridgeport, CT 06602. (Contact: Susan Mann, Mental Health Program)
Associate in Arts Degree in Mental Health with a Specialty in Art Therapy.

KANSAS STATE COLLEGE OF PITTSBURG, Pittsburg, KS 66762. (Contact: Chairman, Department of Art)
Bachelor of Science Degree in Education with a Major in Art Therapy.

MOUNT ALOYSIUS JUNIOR COLLEGE, Cresson, PA 16630. (Contact: Asst. Prof. Vivian Wilkinson, M.Ed., Art Therapy Coordinator)
Associate Degree Program in Art Therapy.

MOUNT MARY COLLEGE, Milwaukee, WI 53222. (Contact: Sr. M. Regine Collins, Chairperson, Art Department)
Undergraduate Program in Art Therapy.

NEW YORK UNIVERSITY, 80 Washington Square East, New York, NY 10003. (Contact: Barbara Polny, Advisor, Department of Art Education)

Undergraduate Program in Art Education with a Concentration in Art Therapy.

PHILADELPHIA COLLEGE OF ART, Broad and Pine Streets, Philadelphia, PA 19102. (Contact: Dolores Francine, Art Therapy Advisor, Liberal Arts Department)
Major in Any Department with Concentration in Art Therapy.

TRENTON STATE COLLEGE, Trenton, NJ 08625. (Contact: Prof. Mark Wilensky, Director of Art Therapy)
Undergraduate Program in Art Therapy.

WILLIAM WOODS COLLEGE, Fulton, MO 65251. (Contact: George E. Tutt, Chairman, Department of Art)
(1) Special Education/Art Therapy, leading to State Certification in Special Education.
(2) Major in Art with a Concentration in Art Therapy.

INSTITUTIONS OFFERING COURSES IN ART THERAPY OR CLOSELY RELATED SUBJECTS

ANTIOCH COLLEGE, Homestead-Montebello Center, 500 N. Caroline Street, Baltimore, MD 21205. (Contact: Prof. Lucille D. Venture)

THE SCHOOL OF THE ART INSTITUTE OF CHICAGO, Michigan Avenue at Adams Street, Chicago, IL 60603. (Contact: Ephraim Weinberg, Chairman, Department of Teacher Education)

BOSTON UNIVERSITY, Metropolitan College, 755 Commonwealth Avenue, Boston, MA 02215. (Contact: Prof. Xenia Lucas)

CALIFORNIA STATE UNIVERSITY, SAN FRANCISCO, 1600 Holloway Avenue, San Francisco, CA 94132. (Contact: Virginia Goldstein, Office of Creative Arts Interdisciplinary)

UNIVERSITY OF CALIFORNIA EXTENSION, SANTA CRUZ, CA 95064. (Contact: Darla Chadima)

COLUMBUS COLLEGE OF ARTS AND DESIGN, 47 North Washington Avenue, Columbus, OH 43215. (Contact: Office of Admissions)

COPPIN STATE COLLEGE, Division of Graduate Studies, 2500 W. North Avenue, Baltimore, MD 21216. (Contact: Prof. Lucille D. Venture)

CREATIVE GROWTH WORKSHOPS, 510 LaGuardia Place, New York, NY 10012. (Contact: Elaine Rapp, ATR, Director)

FOUNDATION FOR ADVANCED EDUCATION IN THE SCIENCES, INC., National Institutes of Health, Bethesda, MD 20014. (Contact: Registrar, NIH, Building 10, Room B1-L-101, Bethesda, MD 20014)

GODDARD COLLEGE, Plainfield, VT 05667. (Contact: Graduate Program Admissions Office, Attention Gladys L. Agell, ATR)

GRAIL, CREATIVE GROWTH THROUGH THE ARTS, P.O. Box 7581, Carmel, CA 93921. (Contact: Grace Forrest, MPS, ATR)

HAWAII LOA COLLEGE, P.O. Box 764, Kaneohe, HI 96744. (Contact: Admissions Office)

HOFSTRA UNIVERSITY, Hempstead, NY 11550. (Contact: Rowena M. Smith, School of Education)

HUNTER COLLEGE, 695 Park Avenue, New York, NY 10021. (Contact: Prof. Elaine Rapp, 510 LaGuardia Place, New York, NY 10012)

INSTITUTE FOR SOCIOTHERAPY, 39 East 20 Street, New York, NY 10003. (Contact: Jean B. Peterson, ACSW, ATR, Division of Community Education)

LINDENWOOD 4, THE LINDENWOOD COLLEGES, St. Charles, MO 63301, St. Louis, MO 63108, Washington, D.C. 20013, Santa Monica, CA 90406. (Contact: Dottie Cohen, MFA, Coordinator of Art Therapy)

UNIVERSITY OF MARYLAND SCHOOL OF SOCIAL WORK AND COMMUNITY PLANNING, 525 West Redwood Street, Baltimore, MD 21201. (Contact: Dr. Aina O. Nucho)

UNIVERSITY OF MASSACHUSETTS, Amherst, MA 01002. (Contact: Continuing Education, Arts Extension Service; or Arts and Humanities Program, School of Education)

MONTEREY PENINSULA COLLEGE, 980 Fremont Street, Monterey, CA 93940. (Contact: Mr. Heinz Hubler, Community Services; or Dr. James Nvette, Psychology Department)

NEW ENGLAND INSTITUTE OF CREATIVE ARTS, 55 Moraine Street, Jamaica Plain, MA 02130. (Contact: Xenia Lucas, Director)

UNIVERSITY OF NEW MEXICO, Albuquerque, NM 87131. (Contact: Howard McConeghey, Chairman, Department of Art Education, College of Education)

NEW ORLEANS CONSORTIUM, Loyola University, 6363 St. Charles Avenue, New Orleans, LA 70118. (Contact: Bob Fleshman, Coordinator, Multiple Arts Therapy Program)

NEW SCHOOL FOR SOCIAL RESEARCH, 66 W. 12th Street, New York, NY 10011. (Contact: Susan Gonick-Barris, ATR, Psychology Department)

NEW YORK ART THERAPY INSTITUTE, 54 West 9th Street, New York, NY 10011. (Contact: Stephen Ross, Director)

NEW YORK INSTITUTE FOR GESTALT THERAPY, 7 West 12th Street, New York, NY 10025. (Contact: Elaine Rapp, ATR, Instructor)

NEW YORK UNIVERSITY, 80 Washington Square East, New York, NY 10003. (Contact: Laurie Wilson, ATR, Department of Art Education)

UNIVERSITY OF NORTHERN COLORADO, Greeley, CO 80631. (Contact: Chairperson, Department of Fine Arts)

OKLAHOMA UNIVERSITY, Off-Campus Classes, 1700 Asp Avenue, Norman, OK 73069. (Contact: Asst. Prof. Margaret C. Howard, ATR; or Dr. Milton Jarrett)

UNIVERSITY OF PITTSBURGH, Pittsburgh, PA 15261. (Contact: Dr. Rivka Sandler, Division of Interdisciplinary Programs, School of Health-Related Professions)

PITTSBURGH CHILD GUIDANCE CENTER, 201 DeSoto Street, Pittsburgh, PA 15213. (Contact: Gloria Miner, Division of Community Services)

SAN DIEGO STATE UNIVERSITY, San Diego, CA 92182. (Contact: Paul A. Lingren, Chairman, Department of Art)

SAN JOSE STATE UNIVERSITY, Office of Continuing Education, San Jose, CA 95192. (Contact: Robert Duman, Associate Director, Extension Services)

SIMMONS COLLEGE, Boston, MA 02215. (Contact: Dr. John Robinson, Department of Education)

SOUTHEASTERN MASSACHUSETTS UNIVERSITY, North Dartmouth, MA 02747. (Contact: Continuing Education Division)

TEACHERS COLLEGE, Columbia University, 525 W. 120th Street, New York, NY 10027. (Contact: Carol Beighley, 31 Park Avenue, White Plains, NY 10603)

TORONTO ART THERAPY INSTITUTE, 216 St. Clair Avenue, West, Toronto, Ontario, Canada. (Contact: Martin A. Fischer, M.D. D. Psych., Executive Director)

TOWSON STATE COLLEGE, Baltimore, MD 21204. (Contact: Chairman, Art Department)

TURTLE BAY MUSIC SCHOOL, 244 E. 52nd Street, New York, NY 10022. (Contact: Jean Mass, Chairman, Arts-in-Therapy Program)

UNIVERSITY OF VERMONT, Burlington, VT 05401. (Contact: Denis Versweyveld, Department of Art, Art Education Program, Attention: Art Therapy)

WEST TEXAS STATE UNIVERSITY, Department of Fine Arts and Arts Education, Canyon, TX 79016. (Contact: Dr. Emilio Caballero, Chairman, Graduate Courses in Art Therapy)

WRIGHT STATE UNIVERSITY, Dayton, OH 45431. (Contact: Dr. Gary Barlow, ATR, Professor and Coordinator, Art Education, 326 Creative Arts Building)

CAPITAL UNIVERSITY, Columbus, Ohio 43209. (Contact: Prof. Richard Phipps)

Overseas Institutions

GRADUATE PROGRAMS

CITY OF BIRMINGHAM POLYTECHNIC, School of Art Education, 26 Priory Road, Birmingham B5 7UQ, England. (Contact: Michael Edwards)
M.A. in Art Education, with special reference to therapeutic and remedial situations. One-year program plus dissertation.

HERTFORDSHIRE COLLEGE OF ART AND DESIGN, 7 Hatfield Road, St. Albans, Hertfordshire, England. (Contact: Mr. J. P. Evans, Head of Remedial Art Dept.)
Certificate in Remedial Art. One-year postgraduate courses offering a qualification for art therapists in Health and Social Services Departments.

MIDDLELOO TRAINING SCHOOL FOR CREATIVE ACTIVITIES AND GROUP WORK, Koningin Wilhelminalaan 1, Amersfoort, The Netherlands. (Contact: M. M. Brom, Director)
Four-Year Courses
Group Work and Use of Creative Activities in Institutional Settings. Creative Therapy with Specializations in Dramatics, Manual Expression, and Music.

INSTITUTIONS OFFERING COURSES
IN ART THERAPY OR CLOSELY RELATED SUBJECTS

HÔPITAL HENRI-ROUSSELLE AND MUTUELLE GÉNÉRALE DE L'EDUCATION NATIONALE, 51 rue Boissière, 75 — Paris 16e, France. (Contact: A. Denner)

NORTHERN IRELAND HEALTH AND SOCIAL SERVICES, E. Section, Belfast B.T.7, Northern Ireland. (Contact: Rita Simon, 11 Bangor Road, Holywood, County Down, Northern Ireland)

POLYTECHNIC OF CENTRAL LONDON, 104-108 Bolsover Street, London, W1, England. (Contact: Secretary, Playspace Trust, c/o Extra-Mural Studies)

QUEENS UNIVERSITY, Belfast, Northern Ireland. (Contact:

Rita Simon, 11 Bangor Road, Holywood, County Down, Northern Ireland)

Compiled by the Education Committee, American Art Therapy Association

Gladys Agell (Chairperson)
Pamela Diamond
Elinor Ulman
Lucille Venture

APPENDIX III:

LITERATURE ON FEATURES TYPICAL OF PICTURES BY INDIVIDUALS OF DIFFERENT PSYCHOPATHOLOGICAL GROUPS

Alschuler, R. H., and Hattwick, L. B. W.: *Painting and Personality: A Study of Young Children,* rev. abr. ed. Chicago, University of Chicago Press, 1969.

Anastasi, A., and Foley, J. P.: An experimental study of the drawing behavior of adult psychotics in comparison with that of a normal control group. *Journal of Experimental Psychology, 34:*169-194, 1944.

Hammer, E. F.: *The Clinical Application of Projective Drawings.* Springfield, Thomas, 1958.

Hanover, M. R.: The *Most Unpleasant Concept Test:* A graphic projective technique. *Journal of Clinical Psychology, 6*(3): 213-233, 1950.

Hellersberg, E.: *The Individual's Relation to Reality in Our Culture: An Experimental Approach by Means of the Horn-Hellersburg Test,* 1st ed. Springfield, Thomas, 1950.

Tolor, A., and Schulberg, H.: *An Evaluation of the Bender-Gestalt Test.* Springfield, Thomas, 1963.

Wachner, J.: Interpretation of spontaneous drawings and paintings. *Genetic Psychological Monographs, 33:*3-70, 1946.

APPENDIX IV:

DENT-KWIATKOWSKA RATING MANUAL
NIMH FAMILY ART EVALUATION STUDY

Instructions for Rating Pictures
"Blind Ratings"

We are asking you to rate pictures drawn during family art evaluation sessions. Not all the pictures you will be rating have been done by patients. Some have been done by other members of the patient's family and some have been done by "control families." Your rating should be "blind." That is, you should not know who drew the picture you are rating. *If you think you know who drew the picture, or which family it is, please don't rate it.*

A word about the procedures and materials used in the family art evaluation sessions. The families can use a black felt tipped pen and/or choose from a spectrum of pastel chalks. Six different sets of instructions are given to them during the sessions. Each picture will be numbered according to the procedure, except that procedure #5 will be grouped with #4 and #6 with #1 since these procedures are rated similarly.

Procedure #1 — *A free picture,* no subject assigned: "Draw whatever comes to mind."

Procedure #2 — *A portrait of the family:* "Draw each member of the family including yourself, not a detailed, photographic resemblance but also more than a matchstick figure."

Procedure #3 — *Abstract family portrait:* "No bodies or features—just use color or shapes to express the way you feel or think about each member of your family, including yourself."

Procedure #4 — *Individual picture from a scribble.* All fami-

234

ly members do arm loosening exercises in preparation for making a scribble as the starting point of a picture. Each then draws his own picture inspired by any line or lines of his scribble.

Procedure #5 — *Joint picture started from a scribble.* Each family member does a second scribble and then, among themselves, they decide which scribble they will use to start a joint picture in which all family members collaborate.

Procedure #6 — *A free picture,* no subject assigned (as in procedure #1), made individually by each family member.

There are no "right" or "wrong" responses to some of the questions; your responses should be based on your own reaction to the pictures or observations of them.

Please inspect the whole picture carefully before beginning to do ratings. This inspection ought to be at a distance of two to four feet.

Unless specified in the code to the contrary, ratings apply to the entire sheet of paper, not to a portion of it. Titles, writing, dates and signatures are considered to be part of the production.

In this study "realism" means the same as representationalism or any representation of recognizable subjects regardless of style, (e.g. stylized, impressionistic, etc.) On the other hand "abstract" is understood as representing no concrete object of nature, but a conception exclusively confined to colors and shapes.

We are concerned with rating various aspects of the picture, not with its pathological significance. Some ratings are labeled (S). This means the response should be based on the raters *OVERALL SUBJECTIVE IMPRESSION* of the picture. This is in contrast to those ratings labeled (A) which require the rater to study the picture and use more *SCRUTINY* in his evaluation.

The code, "−" is used (when given this choice) in those cases where a particular criterion does not apply to the picture in question or when specifically instructed to do so.

In addition to the procedure number, each picture is individually numbered for later identification.

With a response sheet in front of you write your last name, picture number, and procedure number in the upper right hand corner of the response sheet. Just to the left of that enter your rater number.

Rating pictures begins with column 18.

FAMILY ART EVALUATION STUDY

Column No.

1-2	Study No.
3	Card No.
4-8	Family Code (3 letters and 2 digits)
9-14	Individual number (clinical case number)
15	*Procedure No.:*

        1 First Free Picture

        2 Family Portrait

        3 Abstract Family

        4 Scribble

        5 Family Scribble

        6 Last Free Picture

16-17   (These cols. were used to identify the person who rated the pictures)

STUDY PICTURE FULLY. Avoid guessing about whether or not this picture was drawn by a patient. Try to rate each characteristic of the picture independently of the other characteristics.

Column No. 18

    (S) *Comprehensibility* (To be rated without knowledge of title.)

      0 Nothing is recognizable—the picture consists of an amorphous, random coloring, or scribbling.

      1 I can distinguish separate shapes or objects but I cannot guess what the picture is about.

      2 I can make a guess what the picture is about, but on the whole the picture is obscure.

      3 I feel I can make sense out of the picture but it could be seen differently by different persons.

4 I can tell without hesitation what it is and that it couldn't be anything else.

− Family portrait or abstract (2 or 3 in Col. 15)

Code 18 is concerned, in part, with the content of the picture, the *manifest* content not the latent content. You are not expected to treat this picture like an ink blot and try to make something out of it. On the other hand, many of our subjects are not talented and something that looks like Humpty Dumpty may be intended to be a human being and you may sometimes be willing to accept it as such.

For this first rating, the title is covered and you are to make of it what you can without knowing the title. Once you have completed Column 18 and removed the tape blinding, the title becomes an integral part of the picture and is information you can use for all ratings.

Suppose for example that what you thought was a watermelon turns out to be titled "Football." In all subsequent ratings you should use this information if it is applicable in making the various judgements that have to be made.

Suppose, now, you were certain it was a watermelon, and that everyone would recognize it as such (you coded it 4 in Col. 18), and now you find it is a football. Do you go back and change your rating? No. However, you can use this new information when you rate Col. 19 and also when you rate comprehensibility again in Col. 51.

REMOVE TAPE LABELED "TITLE"

Column No. 19

(S) *Meaningfulness of title*

0 There is *no* apparent connection between the subject of the picture and the title.

1 There is a connection but it is (probably) idiosyncratic.

2 There is a connection but the title is overinclusive.

3 There is a connection but the title is literal;

title adds nothing to the understanding of the picture.

4 There is a connection and the title would probably add understanding or interest to the picture, but the title itself is idiosyncratic.

5 There is a connection and the title adds understanding or interest to the picture.

– No title

Code 19. Code may be easier to understand through an illustration: Suppose the picture is of a roasted fowl on a platter apparently ready for carving. Suppose the title were:

"Ho-Hum." This is an "0" since there is no apparent connection to the picture.

"June 1967," or "Aunt Jemima," this would be "1" since one can imagine a connection (cooking, food) but not really be very sure of it.

"Bird" or "Dinner" are "2", overinclusive, since any number of different kinds of pictures would satisfy the title.

"Roast Fowl" is a "3"; it says no more nor no less than the picture.

"Mother's Taste" or "Dad's Job" is coded 4. The connection is clear but the meaning of the title itself is idiosyncratic.

"Dec. 25" or "My Favorite Dish" are examples of a "5". "Roast Turkey" would be a weak "5", almost a "3".

Column No. 20

(S) *Emotional feeling.* Is there any emotion conveyed?

0 There is little or no feeling. Picture is devoid of emotion or expression.

1 There is some feeling but not much.

2 The picture conveys feeling; one can easily imagine emotions being involved in the picture.

Code 20. Emotional feeling, is also a subjective dimension. You do not need to justify your judgment of feeling. However, your own reaction to the picture may be influenced by such things as (1) color, (2) familiarity of subject, (3) the use of shading instead of simple outlines, and so forth. Yet none of these things are essential and some are rated below. So use your own judgment as to how much feeling is conveyed by the picture.

Column No. 21

> (S) *Movement or action.* Does anything seem to be moving or in action?
>
> > 0 There is little or no movement or action in the elements of the picture or the picture as a whole.
> >
> > 1 Some things in the picture, or parts of the picture, can be seen as moving or in action.
> >
> > 2 Most of the picture is seen as involved in movement or action.

IN ALL OF THE FOLLOWING COLOR CODES: Black, white, or gray are considered to be colors if they are used as shading, or coloring, not as outlines only.

Column No. 22

> (A) *Number of colors.* How many different colors are used?
>
> > 0 None (basic lines in black or gray) .
> >
> > 1 One color (Rate this if a color is used for basic lines or throughout the picture) .
> >
> > 2 Two colors.
> >
> > 3 Three colors.
> >
> > 4 Four or more colors.

Column No. 23

> (A) *Color extent.* To what extent is color used? What porportion of the sheet is colored? (The color may be dark or light, weak or intense) .
>
> > 0 Small part; less than one quarter. Most of the paper is not touched by color (Include here pictures which are *only outlined* in black, gray, or a single color) .
> >
> > 1 Roughly half; anywhere from one quarter to

three-quarters.

2 Most of the sheet is colored; more than three quarters; the whole sheet is covered.

Column No. 24

(A) *Dark pigments used?*   (Rate independently of Color Extent) .

0 Mostly light pigments; light combined with medium pigments.

1 Neither dark nor light pigments; medium pigments.

2 Contrasting of dark and other pigments, or a combination.

3 Mostly dark pigments, black, gray, dark brown, dark green, purple (even if only a portion of the page is colored).

– No color; only basic outlines in black or gray.

Code 24. Note the word "mostly." A little bit of gray or dark blue does not make a "0" or a "1" into a "2", nor would a little bit of the "not dark" colors make a "3" into a "2".

Column No. 25

(A) *Intensity of colors.* How heavily is color applied?

0 Very weak (overall washed out or faded effect).

1 Weak (delicate, muted).

2 Neither strong nor weak; medium intensity.

3 Contrasting of strong or weak colors, or a combination.

4 Strong intense colors.

– No color; no shading; only basic outlines in black or gray.

Column No. 26

(S) *Crowdedness* (Picture or some of its parts look overfilled) .

0 Little or no crowdedness. Picture does not feel overfilled.

1 Part of the picture is crowded.
2 Most of the picture is crowded.
3 Entire picture is crowded.

Column No. 27

(A) *Placement off center* (Placement of composition on the sheet) .

0 Not off center
1 Off center, but not all in a corner, or along one of the edges.
2 Very much off center (all in a corner, or along one of the edges) .
– Actually fills whole page

Code 27. Sometimes in a scribble, the original scribble is off-center. Such a scribble is rated as off-center unless additional material is added to center the composition.

Whether the picture is "balanced" is to be rated in Col. 54. Here we are concerned only with the placement of the composition on the sheet of paper.

Column No. 28

(A) *If off-center, in which direction?*

Is it toward the:

1 Top	5 Bottom
2 Upper right	6 Lower left
3 Right	7 Left
4 Lower right	8 Upper left

– Not off center (0 or – in col. 27)

Column No. 29

(S) *Amorphousness*

0 Shapes and/or color areas are well defined; forms are clear and definite even if components of picture are not well integrated into a composition.
1 Some barely discernible shapes and/or forms can be seen but their boundaries are ill defined; if colored in, boundaries are blurred; if out-

lined, tends to be formless.

2 There are no shapes or boundaries; forms are loose, vague and/or blurred.

Code 29. For the purpose of rating amorphousness in a scribble, the rater can ignore the amorphous qualities of the original scribble.

Column No. 30

(S) *Rounded shapes.* Areas of color can be treated as shapes.

0 There are no rounded shapes in the picture, or practically none.

1 There are some rounded shapes in the picture.

2 Most of the shapes in the picture are rounded.

* − There are no shapes in the picture; (code − also for next 4 cols.).

Column No. 31

(S) *Angular shapes.*

0 There are no angular shapes in the picture, or practically none.

1 There are some angular shapes in the picture.

2 Most of the shapes in the picture are angular.

* − There are no shapes in the picture.

Column No. 32

(A) *If angular, acute?*

0 Angles are generally obtuse.

1 Combination of 0 and 2.

2 Angles are generally acute.

− No angular shapes; no shapes (0 in 29 or in 31)

Code 32. Generally speaking, right angles (as in a building, for example) are considered obtuse. However, sometimes a building can be drawn such that it appears as a collection of acute angles.

Column No. 33

(A) *Coloring* in of shapes, objects, persons, or components of objects.

0 No objects are colored in; objects are outlined in black, gray, or a single color.
1 Most objects are outlined, but one or two are colored in.
2 About half are colored in, whether outlined or not in black, gray or color.
3 All or most objects are colored, whether outlined or not in black, gray or color.
4 Some areas are colored so heavily the grain of the paper hardly shows.
− No shapes, no objects.

Code 33. For the word object, one may substitute any of the following: shapes, persons or components of objects, shapes or persons.

Column No. 34

    (S) *Continuity of lines* in the picture. Most of the lines in the picture are:

0 Not continuous; fragmented; dotted; broken lines.
1 Sketchy lines; light discontinuous lines laid on top of or close to each other.
2 Continuous decisive lines but with occasional breaks, leaving occasional openings in the outline of an object or shape.
3 Continuous lines without interruption, or with hardly any interruption.
− There are no lines, just colored areas of color, or complete amorphousness.

Code 34. In judging continuity of lines you may ignore the lines of the original scribble.

Column No. 35

    (A) *Divided picture.* Is there a line drawn *through*

---

*In the actual ratings, this category was used so infrequently that for some analyses a value was assigned based on restudying the picture.

almost the entire composition, not a ground
level, not a horizon? The line need not be a
straight line. If it is diagonal, is it more nearly
vertical or horizontal? Do not code a single line
as "both."

0 No such line

1 Horizontal line(s)

2 Vertical line(s)

3 Both (at least two lines).

Code 35. For a line to be coded as 1 or as 2, it must run through
the composition. A line at the top, bottom or side of the composition is rated 0.

Column No. 36

(S) *Jagged lines.* Are there areas of the picture where
there are jagged lines or where shading is accom-
plished with lines which change direction abruptly?

0 No such lines, practically none.

1 Some jagged lines, and/or jagged shading.

2 A lot of jagged lines, and/or jagged shading.

– There are no lines, just areas of color, or
amorphousness.

Code 36. Jagged lines may be laid on top of each other as shading
or strung out in zigzag, or jagged lines may be running in all
directions. The essence of this dimension is that lines change
direction abruptly. The original lines of the scribble if they present the same characteristic can be coded 1 or 2 as appropriate.

Column No. 37

(A) *Fragmentation*

0 Not fragmented; elements of the picture are related to each other.

1 Some fragmentation but partial organization
through color, form, or meaning.

2 Fragmented except for efforts for organization, e.g. frame, title, or border.

3 Fragmented; unconnected, unrelated elements.

Code 37. The standards for judging fragmentation are different for different procedures, i.e. in an abstract, a series of shapes representing family members may not appear fragmented, but might be so judged in a free picture.

Procedures 2 and 3: Code zero, no fragmentation, if the family members are in a group, i.e. they are close together and share a common orientation or activity. Code 1, some fragmentation, if the family members are presented as completely separate individuals, i.e. are separated by a significant amount of space *or* if (in the family portrait) family members are in different orientations with respect to the viewer *or* if (in the family abstract) there is no apparent relationship between the symbols or shapes used to represent different individuals. *If only one of the conditions mentioned above applies, code a 1.* If more than one of the conditions mentioned above applies, code a 2.

Column No. 38

(A) *Constriction*

0 No constriction; free strokes or bold strokes.

1 Combination of 0 and 2 in one drawing.

2 Constricted; tight; stereotyped.

Code 38. In a "Scribble," the style of the original lines of the scribble is not used as a basis of rating constriction. The picture is considered to be constricted if it is rigidly confined to the original lines of the scribble or to its parts.

Column No. 39

(A) *Indecisiveness* (effort at erasures; starting over— look on back of sheet too.)

0 None

1 Some

2 A lot

Code 39. Indecisiveness is also indicated if lines are drawn and then other lines are drawn in a fashion which indicates indecision as to where they should have been placed in the first instance.

Column No. 40

    (A) *Destructiveness.*

        0 Little or no destructiveness.

        1 Some destructiveness; portions of the picture are smeared or destroyed; title, signature or date occupy major space (do not code this if the title or other writing has the effect of balancing the picture).

        2 Most of the picture is destroyed or smeared.

Column No. 41

    (A) *Other writing* (other than title, signature, date, or requested labeling) .

        0 No writing other than title, signature, date, or requested labeling.

        1 Writing is explanatory; writing is not clearly inappropriate.

        2 Writing is inappropriate; incoherent, or illegible.

Code 41. Use of arrows to point to objects or other symbols can be considered "other writing."

Free Pictures, Family Portraits, and Scribbles

Column No. 42

    (A) *Transparency* in realistic representation.

        0 No transparencies. Include here a case where a single freely drawn stroke extends too far giving an impression of an insignificant transparency.

        1 Minor transparency: in details, e.g. background lines visible; in human figures, hair superimposed on originally sketched circle for head, collar on top of dress.

        2 Major transparency; repeated minor transparen-

cies; basic elements are drawn on top of others, e.g. nude body with clothing or external shape of a house with interior seen through walls.
- No realistic representation; scribble (4 or 5 in Col. 15).

Code 42. In order to code transparency, one must assume that the object in front is opaque. This is a reasonable assumption for such things as clothing unless you are specifically told otherwise. In the case of a cube drawn so that one can see through it, it would be reasonable to assume that it is made of wire, or clear plastic, and therefore, no transparency.

In a scribble, the original lines of the scribble can be ignored in coding transparency.

Column No. 43
   (A) *Distortion* of location, perspective.
     0 No significant distortion.
     1 Minor distortion; distortion as judged by rater as possibly needed for the composition.
     2 Major distortion; mixed profile; parts in the wrong place; dislocation; significant incorrect perspective.
     - No realistic representation.

Column No. 44
   (A) *Disproportions* in realistic representation.
     0 No significant disproportion, components of picture or parts of body are of appropriate size with respect to each other.
     1 Minor disproportion.
     2 Major disproportion.
     - No realistic representation.

Codes 43 & 44. Question 43 and 44 which deal with distortions and disproportions respectively, should be separated to avoid combining them into one question. The latter, "Disproportion" refers to inappropriateness in size of parts of an object related to its whole or of two or more objects or human figures in relation to each other e.g. the picture of one family member occupies the whole page, while another is the size of a match; the person standing next to a house is twice its size, etc. "Distortion," however, infers something to improper location, shape and perspective of parts or whole objects that its effect has a shocking quality. Two points of possible question here—a "mixed profile" is an object or person which looks as if the drawer viewed the object from two or more angles and combined what he saw into one picture, (i.e. side view of a body with a front view of the face or a face viewed simultaneously full faced and in profile).

Column No. 45

> (A) *Incompleteness* — lack of components in realistic representation.
>
> 0 No significant incompleteness.
>
> 1 Minor; lack of background or base; lack of details in secondary components of picture.
>
> 2 Major: Lack of essential characteristics in primary components of picture.
>
> – No realistic representation.

Code 45. Absence of a base or background in a family portrait is not usually considered an incompleteness.

Column No. 46

> (A) *Inappropriate use of colors* in realistic representation.
>
> 0 No significant inappropriate use of colors.
>
> 1 Minor.
>
> 2 Major.
>
> – Outlines only; one color only; black and gray only; no realistic representation.

Family Abstract

Column No. 42

> (A) Degrees of *abstraction* of family abstract.
>
> 0 Not abstract; predominantly human figures,

much like a family portrait.

1 Not abstract; some human figures, or concrete objects (probably used symbolically to represent hobbies or interests).

2 Predominantly abstract; human figures and/or concrete objects are in the minority.

3 Completely abstract; no human figures; no realistic objects.

Column No. 43

(A) *Homogeneity* in family abstract.

0 No homogeneity. Representations are not of the same shape, or of similar colors, or of a theme.

1 Homogeneity primarily of theme. Most family members are represented by their interests, personalities, etc.

2 Homogeneity primarily of shape. Most family members are represented by similar shapes.

3 Homogeneity primarily of color. Most family members are represented by similar colors.

Column No. 44

(A) *Complexity.*

0 Very simple. Most family members are represented by a single color or a single shape, or a simple theme.

1 Somewhat complex. Most family members are represented by combinations of color and shape.

2 Very complex. Most family members are represented by combinations of colors, shapes, lines, symbols, and/or location with respect to each other.

Content Code

(1) The most prominent thing in the picture should be recorded under first content, the second most prominent thing in the next two columns, and so forth.

See pages 258 and 259 for list of items in Content Code.

(2) Note that 00 is not for "no content." Note also that there is no code "–." For no content, use "99." Or use "99" for the second content if there is only one thing in the picture. If there are two things and the second does not match anything on the list, code "98" for second content.

(3) All codes can be read as plural as well as in the singular.

(4) If the most prominent thing in the picture does not match anything on the list, code "98" in the first field, and code the second most prominent thing in the second field. Write the item not coded in "Comment."

(5) Code manifest content in preference to subjective interpretations. Take at face value whatever meaning the title or other writing conveys about the intentions of the person drawing the picture. However, you may code subjective impressions if they fit categories in the list. If you feel you are looking into an enclosed area, you may want to code a "00" or a "20."

(6) The provision of more than one "Content" is to permit you to code more than one object in the picture. It is not for the purpose of coding alternative subjective interpretations of the same object.

(7) A geometric design, "92" is an organized combination of geometric shapes.

Family Portraits

Column No. 47

    (A) *Sex differentiation in drawn figures.*

        0 There are no sex differences in the figures, sex differences are so minimal as to leave doubt about gender of individuals.

        1 There are sex differences — primarily cultural: hair, dress.

        2 There are sex differences — primarily physical: body shape. (By differentiation of body shape is meant such things as genitals; broad shoulders, narrow hips for males; breasts, hips, and narrow waistline for females.)

3 There are sex differences of both types, combination of 1 and 2.

– Does not apply; no human figures drawn.

Column No. 48

(A) *Facial expression — not necessarily human faces.*

0 All or most of the faces have some features but are *expressionless* or ambiguous, or none of the following:

1 Face is *happy;* most faces are *happy.*

2 Face is *sad;* most faces are *sad.*

3 Face is *angry;* most faces are *angry.*

4 Some faces *happy;* some faces *sad.*

5 Some faces *happy;* some faces *angry.*

6 Some faces *sad;* some faces *angry.*

7 Some faces *happy;* some faces *sad;* some faces *angry.*

8 All or most of the faces have *no features.*

– No faces drawn.

Family Portraits and Abstracts

Column No. 49

(A) *Closeness — general.*

0 Family members are presented as individual and separate figures, symbols, or shapes.

1 Some members of the family are in a group or groups, e.g. touching, similar color.

2 The whole family appears as a group or included in a common activity.

Column No. 50

(A) *Closeness — parental.*

0 Parents are separated by at least one other family member.

1 Parents are separated by some object.

2 Parents are placed one next to the other but not

in a "group," e.g. touching or overlapping.
3 Parents are together in a "group," e.g. touching or overlapping.
– Parents are not identifiable in the picture.

Column No. 51

(A) *Prominence* ("other" includes children or pets)

0 No one is particularly prominent; all are about equally prominent; four or more are prominent.
1 One is prominent – father.
2 One is prominent – mother.
3 One is prominent – other.
4 Two are prominent – father and mother.
5 Two are prominent – father and other.
6 Two are prominent – mother and other.
7 Two are prominent – other and other.
8 Three are prominent – father, mother, other.
9 Three are prominent – father, other, other;
— mother, other, other;
— other, other, other.

Column No. 52

(A) *Isolation* ("other" includes children, pets)

0 No one is particularly isolated; all are about equally distanced; four or more are isolated.
1 One is isolated – father.
2 One is isolated – mother.
3 One is isolated – other.
4 Two are isolated – father and mother.
5 Two are isolated – father and other.
6 Two are isolated – mother and other.
7 Two are isolated – other and other.
8 Three are isolated – father, mother, other.
9 Three are isolated – mother, other, other;
— father, other, other;
— other, other, other.

Scribbles Only

Column No. 51

    (A) *Portion used,* of total original scribble.

        0 Less than a quarter of the original scribble is used.

        1 Portion used is between one-fourth and three-fourths.

        2 Over three-fourths of the original scribble is used in the new composition.

        – Impossible to separate original scribble from added lines; impossible to determine how much of original scribble is supposed to be included in the new composition.

    NOTE: "Portion used" refers to the area of the original scribble, not to the number of lines or the length of lines in it.

Column No. 52

    (A) *Additions* to the scribble.

        0 Hardly anything is added to the original scribble.

        1 A few lines and/or color is added.

        2 Lines and/or color is freely added to the scribble to make a composition.

Free Pictures and Scribbles

Column No. 53

    (S) *Comprehensibility*

        0 Nothing is recognizable—the picture consists of an amorphous, random coloring, or scribbling.

        1 I can distinguish separate shapes or objects but I cannot guess what the picture is about.

        2 I can distinguish separate shapes or objects but on the whole the picture is obscure.

        3 I feel I can make sense out of the picture but it could be seen differently by different persons.

4 I can tell without hesitation and feel others could tell what it is and that it couldn't be anything else.

Family Portraits

Column No. 53

(A) *Type of Portrait*

1 Most persons are presented as full figures.

2 Most persons are presented as heads only, or heads and shoulders.

3 Most persons are presented as stick figures.

4 Only one or two persons are drawn; no parents are drawn.

5 Most persons are presented as abstractions.

6 Other than the above; more than one of the above. (Record under "Comments").

Family Abstracts

Column No. 53

(A) *Compartmentalization.* The sheet has been divided into rectangular areas (say, 4, 6, or 8 of them) by drawing lines vertically, or horizontally, or diagonally across the sheet. One box is used for each family member.

0 No compartmentalization; no family members in boxes; only one' family member is presented and he is not in a box.

1 Some family member(s) in box(es).

2 Entire sheet is divided into boxes with one family member in each box.

All Pictures

Cols. 54, 55, 56, 57 are for individual subjective impressions. There is no definitional frame of reference that can be provided. (In "check rating," where two raters are resolving their differences, the procedure for these columns is as follows: If the 2 ratings differ by 2 points, they are averaged. If the 2 ratings differ by 1 point, one of the ratings is chosen at random, e.g. flipping a coin.)

Column No. 54

    (S) *Balance* in form, shapes, colors. (Effect of the entire picture).

    0 Poorly balanced; lopsided.

    1 Balanced; more or less equal distribution of components.

    2 Very well balanced; resulting in harmony and total integration of picture.

Column No. 55

    (S) *Bizarreness* (not merely distorted or disproportioned).

    0 None.

    1 Some.

    2 Definitely bizarre.

Column No. 56

    (S) *Pleasing* qualities? (Individual rater's reaction).

    0 Little or no pleasing qualities.

    1 Some pleasing qualities.

    2 A lot of pleasing qualities.

Column No. 57

    (S) *Displeasing* qualities? (Individual rater's reaction).

    0 Little or no displeasing qualities.

    1 Some displeasing qualities.

    2 A lot of displeasing qualities.

All Pictures

Column No.

58   Pattern: Change in comprehensibility. (4 plus col. 18 minus col. 53). Code "–" for procedures 2 and 3.

59   Pattern: Rater's feeling. (col. 56 plus col. 57).

60   Pattern: Rater's liking.   (2 plus col. 56 minus col. 57).

61-62   Pattern: Irrealism.   (sum of cols. 37, 42, 43, 44, 45, and 46).   Code "blank" "–" if there is a "–" in *more than one* of these columns.   If there is only one "–" in these columns, consider the "–" to be a zero.   Code "blank" "–" for procedure 3.

Column No. 63

   *Detail**

✓   0 Very little detail.

       1 Some detail.

       2 A great deal of fine detail.

       3 The whole picture is in fine detail, even including the background.

Column No. 64

   *Stereotypy**

✓   0 None

       1 Some

       2 A lot

Column No. 65

   *Rigidity in objects or designs presented.**

✓   0 None

       1 Some

       2 A lot

---

*These last three dimensions were added after the rating system had been put in use and coded for only a portion of the pictures.

RATING SHEET FOR DENT-KWIATKOWSKA STUDY

1 2 1

Rater #

Procedure _____ Picture Number _____

Name _____ Date _____

□ 18 Comprehensibility
□ 19 Meaningfulness of title
□ 20 Emotional feeling
□ 21 Movement or action
□ 22 Number of colors
□ 23 Color extent
□ 24 Dark pigments
□ 25 Intensity of colors
□ 26 Crowdedness
□ 27 Placement off center
□ 28 Direction off center
□ 29 Amorphousness
□ 30 Rounded shapes
□ 31 Angular shapes
□ 32 Acute shapes
□ 33 Coloring in
□ 34 Continuity of lines
□ 35 Divided picture
□ 36 Jagged lines
□ 37 Fragmentation
□ 38 Constriction
□ 39 Indecisiveness
□ 40 Destructiveness
□ 41 Other writing

FREE PICTURE:
□ 42 Transparency
□ 43 Distortion
□ 44 Disproportion
□ 45 Incompleteness
□ 46 Inappropriate color
□□ 47-48 Content
□□ 49-50 Content
□□ 51-52 Content
□ 53 Comprehensibility

FAMILY PORTRAIT:
□ 42 Transparency
□ 43 Distortion
□ 44 Disproportion
□ 45 Incompleteness
□ 46 Inappropriate color
□ 47 Sex differentiation
□ 48 Facial expression
□ 49 Closeness - general
□ 50 Closeness - parental
□ 51 Prominence
□ 52 Isolation
□ 53 Type of portrait

ABSTRACT FAMILY:
□ 42 Abstractness
□ 43 Homogeneity
□ 44 Complexity
□□ 45-46 Content
□□ 47-48 Content
□ 49 Closeness - general
□ 50 Closeness - parental
□ 51 Prominence
□ 52 Isolation
□ 53 Compartmentalization

SCRIBBLE:
□ 42 Transparency
□ 43 Distortion
□ 44 Disproportion
□ 45 Incompleteness
□ 46 Inappropriate color
□□ 47-48 Content
□□ 49-50 Content
□ 51 Portion used
□ 52 Additions
□ 53 Comprehensibility

ALL PICTURES
□ 54 Balance
□ 55 Bizarreness
□ 56 Pleasing
□ 57 Displeasing

Comments: _____
_____
_____
_____

58 60 62
63 Detail
64 Stereotypy
65 Rigidity

Column	**Free Pictures, Family Abstracts,**
No.	**and Scribbles**

(See   (A) Content, first (Code most prominent)
Rating   (A) Content, second (Code second most prominent)
Sheet)   (A) Content, third (Code third most prominent)

Inanimate objects in nature:
00 Open, empty space
    (landscape)
01 Cave, inside
02 Sun, sunshine
03 Moon
04 Star (celestial)
05 Cloud, dark
06 Cloud, not 05
07 Mountains, jagged or icy
08 Mountains, hills,
    rounded
09 Fertile fields
10 Water, calm
11 Water, moving but not
    rough
12 Water, rough

Natural phenomena:
15 Snow
16 Rain
17 Fire or flame
18 Smoke
19 Lightning

Man-made objects:
20 Inside of corridor or
    room
21 Road, path
22 Fence
23 Tall building

24 House, shelter
25 Means of conveyance,
    surface (car, boat, train)
26 Means of conveyance,
    air
27 Machine
28 Recreational item; sport
    item
29 Weapon
30 Empty food or drink
    container
31 Food or drink container
    (not 30)
32 Container, not 30 or 31
33 Food (except raw fruit)
34 Drink
35 Clothing
36 Home furnishings

Vegetable world:
40 Dead flower or tree
41 Flower, not 40
42 Tree with leaves,
    needles
43 Tree without leaves or
    leaves not visible
44 Raw fruit
45 Grass

Animal world (except man):

50 Dead insect, butterfly or bird
51 Insect, except a butterfly
52 Butterfly in flight
53 Butterfly, not 50 or 52
54 Bird at rest, not a bat or bird of prey
55 Bird in flight, not a bat or bird of prey
56 Bird of prey, in flight or at rest
57 Bird, not 50, 54, 55, or 56
58 Fish, fierce
59 Fish, not 58
60 Dead animal
61 Animal, cuddly or friendly
62 Animal, fierce
63 Animal, not 60, 61, or 62

Parts of animal or human:

80 Anatomical parts or insides
81 Eye; staring eye
82 Nose, chin or teeth, over-sized, exaggerated
83 Mouth, large or exagger-ated
84 Genitals; pubic hair
85 Rounded object, at least 3 times long as broad, not part of a structure

Other:

86 Imaginary or cartoon, friendly
87 Imaginary animal or car-toon, not 86
88 Religious symbol
89 Other symbol

Human:

70 Dead human
71 Human figure, nude or nearly nude
72 Human figure, clothed
73 Human figure, not 71 or 72
74 Human face, happy
75 Human face, sad
76 Human face, angry
77 Human face, frightened
78 Human face, not 74, 75, 76 or 77

Abstraction:

90 Geometric shape, unshaded
91 Geometric shape, shaded
92 Geometric design
93 Free form, unshaded
94 Free form, shaded
95 Abstraction, none of above or combination of above

98 Contents, but not codeable (Write in "Comments")
99 No content

APPENDIX V:

PART I.

Instructions: Study each picture carefully, read the operational definition and rate each picture in turn on each variable. Go through the entire series of pictures for one variable and then go on to the next variable, starting the series over. *DO NOT RATE EACH PICTURE ON ALL THREE VARIABLES AT THE SAME TIME.*

    1. *Integration.*

        1 = The picture as a whole is well integrated; the parts go together and transmit a feeling of unity, organization and wholeness.

        2

        3 = Major parts of the picture are vague, poorly defined or split off and unrelated to the rest of the picture. These parts detract from the picture's unity, wholeness or definitiveness.

        4

        5 = The picture is almost entirely vague, shows poorly defined boundaries, barely discernible shapes and is organized very poorly, or it may be divided into a number of separate, totally unrelated parts each of which may be within itself defined.

        0 = Cannot rate

    2. *Understandability.*

        1 = The picture immediately transmits to the viewer a meaning or clear representation of its content. The viewer's own subjective response (if different than the immediately conveyed meaning) should not be rated.

2

3 = The picture conveys a meaning but one which is open to multiple interpretations.

4

5 = The picture is not understandable, no meaning is conveyed by it unless the viewer adds his own ideas or interpretation.

0 = Cannot rate

3. *Use of colors.*

1 = Good — 5 colors or more; or several colors blended, shaded; good balance of light and dark colors; or most of the sheet colored.

2

3 = Fair — Two to four colors used either in linear form or for coloring or shading.

4

5 = Poor — Only outlines in black or gray, or only one color used in addition to the outlines.

0 = Cannot rate

PART II
Instructions: Look at each family portrait and score it for body image.

4. *Body Image* — Rate each person represented in the picture separately

1 = Good — All parts of the body represented.

2

3 = Fair — Correct representation of heads only or body with missing hands or feet or details. Parts which are appropriately missing, e.g. feet under a counter, should not be scored as missing.

4

5 = Poor — Heads with no features, main parts of body missing, match-stick figures, transparency.

0 = Cannot rate

Now look at each abstract family portrait and score it in level of abstraction.

5. *Level of Abstraction*

For the purpose of rating this variable the process of abstraction is defined as follows: It is the ability to portray qualities in other than purely representational terms. That is, the subject is able to represent qualities of personality or feeling states without the use of an actual human figure. In other words he is able to extract and transform these qualities so that an actual stimulus figure is not necessary.

1 = Good — Ability to represent feelings, personalities and/or relationships abstractly by means of non-representational (geometrical, or undefined) shapes and/or colors.

2

3 = Fair — Representation of abstract concepts through concrete symbols — e.g. drawings of hobbies, sports, or interests as representing personalities. Any representation of an object, as object, should be scored as a concrete symbol.

4

5 = Poor — Complete inability to use abstract concepts, e.g. the family member draws naturalistic human figures and may distort or change some of its shape or color. No relationships, feelings, or personality characteristics are described by the figures as represented (stick figures arranged in a row are scored 5).

0 = Cannot rate

PART III.

Material in part III is arranged into sets of three for each individual.

Instructions: Score each *set* on each of the variables. As before, score all sets in one variable before going on to the next one. *DO NOT SCORE A SET FOR ALL THREE VARIABLES AT ONCE.*

6. *Creative resources.*

1 = Good — All three pictures show one or more of the following: rich, colorful, imaginative, interesting or expressive.

2

3 = Fair — One or more pictures have the qualities above, others clearly do not. The whole series does not impress in particular (a neutral quality).

4

5 = Poor — Paucity of imagination, expressiveness — leaves you with impression of dullness or emptiness (a somewhat negative quality).

0 = Cannot rate

PART IV.

Instructions: Rate each family on each of the following variables using the summary of the entire session and their joint scribble. Each family should be rated on the variables before going on to the next family.

7. *Subjective responses of rater to pictures and behavior throughout the session.*

1 = Positive response.

2

3 = Essentially neutral response.

4

5 = Negative response.

0 = Cannot rate

8. *Ability to work on a joint task (rate the family unit).*

1 = Positive interaction between most of the family members or constructive directions given or accepted throughout most of the session.

2

3 = Most family members shifting from active to marginal participation in the group task.

4

5 = Most family members detached from joint task or un-

cooperative with others, or undermining (one may actually follow the instructions and complete the task on the whole jointly — the family unit should still be rated a 5).

0 = Cannot rate

9. *Individuation.*

1 = Usually (most often) separate, i.e. independent, but communicating with each other.

2

3 = Clearly dependent dyads or triads set up but with some effort for separateness and/or most members isolated but with some effort for closeness.

4

5 = All family members dependent on one or more other family members or all members isolated, not communicating about the task.

0 = Cannot rate

10. *Involvement.*

1 = Mostly positive involvement with each other.

2

3 = Involvement shifting with withdrawal between family members.

4

5 = A majority of family members withdraw from others throughout the session.

0 = Cannot rate

11. *Alliances* (interpersonal bonds).

1 = Solid, positive alliances between all family members.

2

3 = Positive alliances with some of the family members and negative with others, or shifting.

4

5 = No clear alliances or only hostile, negative ones.

0 = Cannot rate

12. *Ability of the family to focus attention on the task, to fol-*

low instructions and to produce jointly a complete picture. (Rate the family only as it performed on the joint scribble).

1 = The picture answers the requirements of the procedure, is well organized and complete.

2

3 = The treatment of the picture is tentative, the task is only partially understood; leaving a part incomplete; focusing on irrelevant details or on a fragment of the picture.

4

5 = Incapacity to understand the task and complete inability to achieve it following the given instructions.

0 = Cannot rate

RATING SHEETS FOR TWIN STUDY

Variable	Mother	Father	Parental total	(Identified I Patient)	(Control C Patient)	Twin total	Family total
Section I. Ratings of Each First and Last Free Picture and Individual Scribbles (36 Pictures)							
1. Integration N D C							
2. Understandability N D C							
3. Use of color N D C							
Overall totals N D C							

Variable	Section II. Ratings of Each Family Portrait (12 Pictures) and Each Abstract Family Portrait (12 Pictures)						
	Mother	Father	Parental total	(Identified I Patient)	(Control C Patient)	Twin total	Family total
4. Body Image N D C							
5. Abstraction N D C							
Overall totals N D C							

Variable	Section III. Ratings of Each Individual's Set of First and Last Free Pictures and Individual Scribbles (12 Sets of 3 Pictures)						
	Mother	Father	Parental total	(Identified I Patient)	(Control C Patient	Twin total	Family total
6. Creative resources N D C							

Variable	Section IV. Ratings of Each Joint Scribble with Narrative Summary (3 Pictures)		
	(Normal) N	(Discordant) D	(Concordant) C
7. Rater response			
8. Interaction			
9. Individuation			
10. Involvement			
11. Alliances			
12. Task focus			
Total			

REFERENCES

1. Naumburg, M. *Studies of the "free" art expression of behavior problem children and adolescents as a means of diagnosis and therapy.* (rev. ed.) New York: Teachers College Press, 1973.
2. Naumburg, M. *Schizophrenic art: its meaning in psychotherapy.* New York: Grune and Stratton, 1950.
3. Kwiatkowska, H. Y., and Perlin, S. *A schizophrenic patient's response in art therapy to changes in the life of the psychotherapist.* DHEW Publication No. NIH-33807. Bethesda, Maryland: Public Health Service, 1959.
4. Beels, C. C., and Farber, A. "Family therapy: a view." *Family Process,* 1969, *8,* 280-332.
5. Mosher, L. R., and Kwiatkowska, H. Y. "Family art evaluation: use in families with schizophrenic twins." *Journal of Nervous and Mental Disease,* 1571, *153,* 165-179.
6. Sinrod, H. "Communication through paintings in a therapy group." *Bulletin of Art Therapy,* 1964, *3,* 133-147.
7. Green, H. *I never promised you a rose garden.* New York: Holt, Rinehart and Winston, 1964.
8. Kwiatkowska, H. Y. "Family art therapy and family art evaluation: indication and contraindication," in Jakab, I. (Ed.). *Psychiatry and Art* (Vol. 3). Basel:Karger, 1971.
9. Minuchin, S. "Conflict-resolution in family therapy," in Haley, J. (Ed.). *Changing families: a family therapy reader.* New York: Grune and Stratton, 1971.
10. Kwiatkowska, H. Y. "Family art therapy: experiments with a new technique." *Bulletin of Art Therapy,* Spring, 1962.
11. Harlow, H. F., and Zimmerman, R. R. "Affectional responses in the infant monkey." *Science,* 1959, *130,* 3373.
12. Elkisch, P. "The 'scribbling game'—a projective method." *The Nervous Child,* 1948, *7,* 247.
13. Cane, F. *The artist in each of us.* New York: Pantheon Books, 1951.
14. Naumburg, M. *Psychoneurotic art: its function in psychotherapy.* New York: Grune and Stratton, 1953.
15. Kwiatkowska, H. Y. "Family art therapy." *Family Process,* 1967, *6,* 37-55.
16. Day, J., and Kwiatkowska, H. Y. "The psychiatric patient and his 'well' sibling: a comparison through their art productions." *Bulletin of*

Art Therapy, 1962, *2,* 51-66.

17. Schaffer, L.; Wynne, L. C.; Day, J.; Ryckoff, I. M.; and Halperin, A. "On the nature and sources of the psychiatrist's experience with the family of the schizophrenic." *Psychiatry,* 1962, *25,* 32-45.

18. Ulman, E. "A new use of art in psychiatric diagnosis." *Bulletin of Art Therapy, 1965, 4,* 91-116.

19. Burns, R. C., and Kaufman, S. H. *Kinetic Family Drawings (K-F-D): an introduction to understanding children through kinetic drawings.* New York: Brunner/Mazel, 1970.

20. Kwiatkowska, H. Y. "The use of families' art productions for psychiatric evaluation." *Bulletin of Art Therapy,* 1967, *6,* 52-69.

21. Kwiatkowska, H. Y.; Day, J.; and Wynne, L. C. *The schizophrenic patient, his parents and siblings: observations through family art therapy.* Catalogue of exhibit presented at the Annual Meeting of the American Psychiatric Association, 1962. U. S. Department of Health, Education, and Welfare: Public Health Service.

22. Wynne, L. C., and Singer, M. T. "Schizophrenic impairments of shared focal attention." Paper presented at the Tenth Annual Bertram Roberts Memorial Lecture, Yale University, April 26, 1967.

23. Winnicott, D. W.: "Transitional objects and transitional phenomena," in *Collected papers.* New York: Basic Books, 1961.

24. Kwiatkowska, H. Y., and Harris, H. G. "Blind evaluations of pictures in family art psychotherapy: their communicative power." Paper presented at the Annual Meeting of the American Psychiatric Association, Washington, D.C., May 4, 1971.

25. Guggenheim, F. C.; Pollin, W.; Stabenau, J. R.; and Mosher, L. R. "Prevalence of physical illness in parents of identical twins discordant for schizophrenia." *Psychosomatic Medicine,* 1969, *31,* 288-299.

26. Mosher, L. R.; Pollin, W.; and Stabenau, J. R. "Families with identical twins discordant for schizophrenia: some relationships between identification, thinking styles, psychopathology, and dominance-submissiveness." *British Journal of Psychiatry,* 1971, *118,* 29-42.

27. Stabenau, J. R.; Pollin, W.; Mosher, L. R.; Frohman, C.; Friedhoff, A. J.; and Turner, W. "Study of monozygotic twins discordant for schizophrenia. Some biologic variables (lactate-pyruvic ratio; 3,4-dimethoxyphenylethylamine; S_{19} macroglobulin; antirabbit red cell hemagglutinin; protein bound iodine)." *Archives of General Psychiatry,* 1969, *20,* 145-158.

BIBLIOGRAPHY

Bing, E. "The conjoint family drawing." *Family Process*, 1970, *9*, 173-194.

Day, J., and Kwiatkowska, H. Y. "The psychiatric patient and his 'well' sibling." *Bulletin of Art Therapy*, Winter, 1962.

Dent, J. K., and Kwiatkowska, H. Y. "Aesthetic preference of young adults for pictures drawn by mental patients and by members of their immediate family." *Science de l'Art*, 1971.

Garai, S. H., and Garai, J. E. "Techniques of family art therapy." *Group*, 1974, 1 and 5.

Garcia, V. L. "Case study: family art evaluation in a Brazilian guidance clinic." *American Journal of Art Therapy*, 1975, *14*, 132-139.

Harriss, M., and Landgarten, H. "Art therapy as an innovative approach to conjoint treatment: a case study." *Art Psychotherapy*, 1973, *1*, 221-228.

Kraft, A., and Austin, V. "Art therapy in the educational use of multiple impact theory," in Jakab, I. (Ed.). *Psychiatry and art*, Proceedings of 4th International Colloquium, Psychopathology of Expression, Washington, D.C., 1966, 106-115.

Kwiatkowska, H. Y. "Family art therapy and family art evaluation: indication and contraindication," in Jakab, I. (Ed.). *Psychiatry and art* (Vol. 3). Basel: Karger, 1971.

Lachman, M.; Stuntz, E. C.; and Jones, N. "Art therapy in the psychotherapy of a mother and her son." *American Journal of Art Therapy*, 1975, 14, 105-116.

Landgarten, H. "Group art therapy for mothers and daughters." *American Journal of Art Therapy*, 1975, *14*, 121-126.

Levick, M. "Family art therapy in the community." *Philadelphia Medicine*, 1973, *69*, 7.

Levick, M., and Herring, J. "Family dynamics as seen through art therapy." *Art Psychotherapy*, 1973, *1*, 45-54.

Muller, E. "Family group art therapy: treatment of choice for a specific case," in Jakab, I. (Ed.). *Psychiatry and art*, Proceedings of 4th International Colloquium, Psychopathology of Expression, Washington, D. C., 1966, 132-143.

Rubin, J. A.; Magnussen, M. G.; and Bar, A. "Stuttering: symptom-system-symbol—art therapy in the treatment of a case of disfluency," in Jakab, I. (Ed.), *Psychiatry and art* (Vol. 4). Basel: Karger, 1975.

Rubin, J. A., and Magnussen, M. G. "A family art evaluation." *Family Process*, 1974, *13*, 185-200.

Sherr, C., and Hicks, H. "Family drawings as a diagnostic and therapeutic technique." *Family Process,* 1978, *12,* 439.

Wadeson, H. S. "Art techniques used in conjoint marital therapy." *American Journal of Art Therapy,* 1973, *12,* 147-164.

Wadeson, H. S. "Conjoint marital art therapy techniques." *Psychiatry,* 1972, *35,* 89.

Wadeson, H. S. "The fluid family in multi-family art therapy." *American Journal of Art Therapy,* 1976, *15,* 115.

Wadeson, H.S., and Fitzgerald, R. G. "Marital relationship in manic-depressive illness." *Journal of Nervous and Mental Disease,* 1971, *153,* 180.

Zierer, E.; Sternberg, D.; Finn, R.; and Farmer, M. "Family creative analysis: its role in treatment. Part 1." *Bulletin of Art Therapy,* 1966, *5,* 47.

Zierer, E.; Sternberg, D.; Finn, R.; and Farmer, M. Family creative analysis: its role in treatment. Part II." *Bulletin of Art Therapy,* 1966, *5,* 87.

NAME
INDEX

SUBJECT
INDEX

273